SCIENCE PROJECTS HANDBOOK

EDITED BY SHIRLEY MOORE
Science Clubs of America

Science Service * Washington
Ballantine Books * New York

091 02

Science Service, Inc.

1719 N St., N.W., Washington 6, D. C.

Ballantine Books, Inc.

101 Fifth Ave., New York 3, N. Y.

CONTENTS

CONTENTS

CONTENTS

A Matter of Credit

MANY HANDS and minds have cooperated on this book, and we list the staff of the Youth Division of Science Service for particular mention: Dorothy Schriver, Assistant Director for Administration; Joseph H. Kraus, Coordinator of National Science Fair-International; Leslie Watkins, Executive Secretary of Science Clubs of America; Shirley Moore, Youth Editor; and also some of the editorial staff of Science Service, especially Judith Viorst.

Science Service is the Institution for the Popularization of Science. It was organized in 1921 as a nonprofit corporation.

Some of a grant from the National Science Foundation has been utilized to allow the sending of copies of this book to the 25,000 teacher-sponsors of Science Clubs of America and the several thousand more cooperators who conduct the more than 200 regional science fairs that participate in National Science Fair-International. The National Science Youth Program of Science Service includes Science Clubs of America, National Science Fair-International and the National Science Talent Search for the Westinghouse Science Scholarships.

WATSON DAVIS
Director, Science Service

Chapter 1 • BECOMING A SCIENTIST

IT WOULD be hard to imagine a more exciting time than now to be choosing a future! The greatest adventures and the bravest dreams of this Age of Space are still to be realized—and you can decide to join the exploring parties. You even may lead a new adventure of your own.

There is still time to get ready. There is time to find out where you fit and to train yourself to make the most of whatever abilities you may have. There is time, too, to discover that the scientific community has a good many roads leading to it and a truly magnificent variety of architecture to choose from once you get there.

Scientists often are thought of as people of incandescent genius who brood in solitary towers, and some of them do, of course. But scientists are as likely to be found in modern glass-walled buildings, where they work companionably with large numbers of people. Scientists and technicians may operate as teams in extensive series of laboratories or they may choose to work in offices, or classrooms, or in shops filled with massive equipment, or in open fields and forests, or on mountains and oceans.

As a matter of fact, a person can be some kind of a scientist, engineer or technologist in nearly any corner of the world he prefers and under whatever circumstances fit him best.

What Is a Scientist?

Because the word *scientist* has developed such blurred edges, it may be helpful to look at word pictures of science and scientists sketched by people who have good reason to know what a scientist is and does.

Scientists are trained specialists who have "fresh, unorthodox, nimble and vibrating minds," according to Dr. Warren Weaver, a former officer of the Rockefeller Foundation.

Looking back on many years of interpreting science and scientists to the reading public, Dr. Watson Davis, director of Science Service, comments, "If one views the extensive and sympathetic play that science gets in the press, magazines, radio and TV today, it is hard to realize that not long ago the scientist to the cartoonist was a funny old man with a beard, and the way to report a scientific meeting was to pick out the big words in the program and write a funny story. Now, both the public and the press show a lively appreciation of scientists as interesting, infinitely varied human beings whose work is providing invaluable clues to the future."

Mark W. Cresap, Jr., president of Westinghouse Electric Corporation, says, "It is the scientists who now face the great frontiers; theirs is a unique world-wide fraternity dedicated to the mastery of nature, not the mastery of man; in them we find the vision and spirit and purpose which have constituted the elements of leadership in the past."

Dr. Anne Roe, noted researcher at Harvard University, has devoted some years to studying what makes a scientist. She says, "What nonscientists do not realize is that science is fun, that there are few, if any, emotional experiences so profound, so satisfying, so beautiful, as seeing a pattern where there was none before, as finding an answer to a question asked long ago, as finding a new question to ask."

Dr. Edward Teller, famous University of California physicist, agrees that science is fun to a scientist. "You have the fun of being thoroughly absorbed in what you are doing. And you have the fun of working for a clear-cut decision," he says.

To put it another way, it might be said that a scientist is a searcher who, more than anything else, enjoys trying to find new facts, new relationships, new ways to do things, new materials and ways to use them, new understanding of biology, physics, chemistry, mathematics, astronomy, space science, oceanography, weather or any other theoretical or practical field of inquiry under and including the sun.

What Makes a Student-Scientist?

Most teen-agers who want very much to become scientists are driven by an irresistible need to explore and to know. When they are asked about their plans for the future, the annual winners of the Science Talent Search for the Westinghouse Science Scholarships and Awards, conducted by Science Clubs of America, come up with fairly awe-inspiring goals. Sharing many adult researchers' sense of standing on the brink of a major breakthrough, a great many of them want to join the search for a really usable general theory that will bring together sections of knowledge about the nature of matter, atomic structure, basic mathematics and so on.

The future physicists want to look into particle and atmospheric physics. Many are attracted by the newest departures in biophysics, biochemistry and the uses of mathematics and electronics in biological research. Several belong to the space-happy brotherhood and want to advance man's drive toward the stars by carrying out research on rockets, trajectories, ballistics, space medicine and other problems of space exploration.

Some are alight with such ideas as finding better and cheaper ways of producing abundant power for individual and industrial use, as well as for space travel; some want to ferret out the last secrets of cancer and the chemical processes of life. Others want to discover brand-new materials, new mathematics theorems, or methods of verifying and studying what are called "psi" forces. A great many hope ultimately to contribute to world peace through their research, and many describe an unquenchable interest in what one boy called "the fundamental question of why."

A variety of influences have led these high school seniors to such goals. Some of the most important are dedicated teachers, inspiring and helpful scientists, stimulating and sympathetic family backgrounds, and books, magazines and scientific journals. Other factors that led these students to choose careers in science were science projects and science fairs—exhibitions of students' projects, demonstrations, collections, inventions and experiments. For others, the realization of individual scientific ability, trips to places that awakened intellectual curiosity, and scientific equipment and kits that introduced challenging possibilities were the important influences.

Forty percent of the top forty winners of the Nineteenth Science Talent Search named teachers as having been especially influential in their development; thirty percent named scientists, some of whom are university professors; and twenty-five percent credited members of their families.

Describing the way in which her teacher helped her, one of the girls said, "She taught me to think things out for myself and develop new procedures instead of trying vainly to follow stereotyped ones which were not feasible in our laboratory."

A scientist impressed his young protégé as "one of the major influences in causing me to conduct research and not just to study."

One boy discovered for himself that science was "the most philosophically satisfying method for really finding things out."

This group reported that their decisions to chart their lives toward careers in science were made at ages ranging from very early childhood to age seventeen. Some of them had never even considered any other future; others said that the idea matured gradually, with no special period of deciding. A quarter of the group began at thirteen years of age to look forward to becoming professional scientists.

Can You Be a Scientist?

When you read and hear about students who have won national honors for their achievement and promise in science, perhaps you feel a little hesitant. Daydreaming about the fascinating realm of the unpredictable, where important answers are found because somebody wondered how it would be if things were not as they seem so obviously to be, possibly you question your own qualifications. Do you, after all, have any reason to believe you could have a place in this exciting world?

Maybe mathematics and physics remain mysteries to you, no matter how hard you batter your brain. Or maybe your hands behave like unwieldy feet when you try to solder a delicate electronic circuit or mount a nearly invisible insect. Maybe you would be happier if you never saw the inner workings of an animal; maybe a trickle of blood makes you remember an urgent errand elsewhere.

Fortunately, all the maybe's seldom belong to one person. While math and physics may elude you, you may be very expert with the soldering gun or the insect collection. Or if you do have hands like boxing gloves, perhaps it is your special joy to roam the hills and valleys looking for mineral specimens or fossils or Indian artifacts.

Although most of the profoundly creative discoveries will be made by research scientists of very unique quality, the world has and expects to find only a few of these individuals. You may, of course, discover that you have been born with this potential quality, and you may choose to undertake the long and rigorous training necessary to develop and mature it. On the other hand, there is need for thousands of top-level scientists, engineers and technologists. There must be large numbers of dedicated experimental scientists and many technical assistants to work with researchers in laboratories to produce tomorrow's miracles.

If your special gift is a talent for working with people, you might become an administrator in a scientific organization. Or you might be a science teacher, one of the most rewarding and vitally necessary of the science professions. For this you will want very solid background in your subject, plus that magic ingredient of personal enthusiasm and the ability to share it with your students.

Science writing, scientific illustration and the designing of science courses and demonstrations are comparatively new and important fields that demand still different talents and orientation.

New understanding and its practical benefits are almost never accomplished alone. The distinguished scientists who win world acclaim are quick to minimize their personal achievement, emphasizing the immeasurable contribution of their co-workers and predecessors. And so, if you are genuinely interested in some field or activity of the scientific community, and have the capacity to work hard and carefully, with perseverance and concentration you can discover a niche in science, whether or not you come within shouting distance of being a genius.

There are, of course, ways to share in the adventure of science without necessarily being a scientist yourself. For instance, scientific illustration, science library work, science writing and editing or secretarial and administrative assistant jobs in scientific organizations have been done with great success by nonscientists. Some background in at least one of the sciences is helpful in such jobs, but it is possible to pick up the necessary vocabulary and specialized knowledge.

When it comes right down to it, maybe you should not be and never will be a scientist. The world would be strangely askew if everyone suddenly joined one profession and there were no businessmen, grocers, designers, steelworkers, artists, poets, lawyers and all the rest. But if you never do even five minutes of work in the sciences, your life will be immeasurably richer in whatever profession you choose if you have an appreciative understanding and lively interest in what goes on in the scientific community.

One of the most urgent needs of the Space Age is for citizens of broadly balanced perspective who are informed and alert to scientific problems, developments and solutions.

Clues to Scientific Ability

Authorities in the field believe that many potential scientists have been lost because they had no idea of their own capabilities until it was rather too late to do anything about training them. Studies of successful scientists and engineers have suggested some useful criteria that you might want to use as a general guide in judging yourself.

For example, Frank W. Eller of the Science Manpower Project at Columbia University reports that a teen-ager's potential as an engineering student may be considered good if he is in the top third of his group in mathematics and science courses and in standardized mathematical achievement tests, scores about 100 on IQ tests, and shows several of the following qualities: general and technical vocabulary ability, interest in science and technology and in related hobbies, participation in science competitions, membership in science organizations, ability to comprehend scientific materials and to visualize solid objects from flat plans, friendship with scientists and technologists, good work and study habits.

A study of successful engineering students suggests such additional characteristics as admiration for science teachers; interest in chess, puzzles and riddles; preference for individual sports as opposed to team activity; lively curiosity and the use of a cause-and-effect approach.

Some of the clues to identifying embryo research scientists include such characteristic traits and aptitudes as walking and/or talking early in childhood and quickly acquiring a rather sophisticated vocabulary. Some learn to read, pretty much on their own, before they go to school. They usually ask more (and harder to answer) questions than average. They not only understand the answers immediately, but store fairly incredible quantities of information in their heads. Numbers, maps, encyclopedias, dictionaries and telephone directories are frequently more fascinating to them than attractive books designed for children.

When they enter school, they usually become inveterate readers. Their interests range over many fields, and they are usually superior students. They develop qualities of leadership, self-control, self-discipline, persistence and intellectual honesty—unless something goes sadly wrong along the way.

Although they are often above average physically and socially, they are not usually enthusiastic about group sports like football and baseball, or about other mass activities and entertainment. Most of them prefer tennis, cycling, walking, reading, music, school club activities, social dancing, chess, bridge, math games and puzzles.

Various investigators have turned up other guideposts to scientific talent, such as ability to read about two years above grade level, mature moral attitudes, versatility in ability and interests, good spacial visualization and a combination of self-confidence and introversion.

Some additional traits drawn from evaluation studies of winners of the annual Science Talent Search are intense intellectual curiosity, ingenuity and an intuitive grasp of why and how facts may relate to each other. The most creative scientists may work slowly in gathering and analyzing data, but then move swiftly toward a solution.

According to some authorities, the dominant characteristic of the outstanding scientist is a fierce independence. These talented individuals often feel themselves to be different from other people and they are less likely to be concerned with conventional values and goals.

Obviously not all successful scientists fit these measuring sticks, since scientists come in all flavors, just as artists or mechanics or bankers do. And there are many instances of late bloomers who showed little evidence of interest or talent in science until they were in college, graduate school or even in mid-career. Such a highly contributive scientist as Dr. Wernher von Braun, of space and missile fame, is reported to have confessed to a Congressional Committee that he flunked both mathematics and physics when he was twelve or thirteen years old. "But," he said, "I picked them up later."

Building Your Future

Naturally the place to begin building your future is in the place where you are right now.

If you are in junior or senior high school, for instance, you can take a second look at the courses you plan to schedule. If you have not included all the mathematics and science you can fit in, perhaps there is still time to do so. If it seems that you have passed the point of no return for some of these, possibly you can take them in concentrated form at summer sessions. The study of foreign languages is also valuable, for you may wish to read scientific magazines and books that have not been translated into English.

You should pay special attention to the periodical sections of your school and public libraries, just to be sure that you have not been missing some interesting and authoritative scientific magazines and journals that will keep you informed on current developments. Most libraries have increased the number of such publications kept regularly on the shelves and have greatly expanded the selection of science books and reference materials.

You can be alert to scientific meetings, lectures, science fairs, demonstrations, tours, seminars, congresses, clubs and all the other opportunities that may exist in your community.

When you join such activities, you also may find opportunities to talk to scientists and teachers who are working in the fields that interest you most. Such personal contacts with working scientists will give you a sort of three-dimensional feeling about science and scientists that would be difficult to get in any other way.

In all your curriculum planning, reading and leisure science activities you should guard against overly narrow specialization. So much of modern science crosses the lines between scientific disciplines that you will want to have some background in several. A broad sampling of fields will give you a better base for choosing your eventual career, too, for even college and graduate students find their interests and perspective changing as they penetrate more deeply into various specialties.

To all of this you will want to add both breadth and depth in the humanities in order to be a fully developed individual with balanced insight and appreciation.

You can make sure that you are doing everything possible to prepare for further training when you have finished high school. Whether you look forward to technical school or to college, you will want to survey all of the possibilities and to be ready to apply for admission in plenty of time. This, by the way, can be done during the junior year of high school, because an increasingly large number of colleges are offering early admission.

If you need or want a scholarship to help you go to college, you will want to start your planning early, discussing your ideas and hopes with your family and your high school guidance counselor. Your counselor will have detailed information on many colleges and scholarships, and can tell you about any special aptitude tests or interviews that must take place early in your senior year. If your school does not have a guidance counselor, the school library and the public library may have collections of college catalogs and scholarship leaflets. When you have narrowed your possible choice to, say, five or six colleges, write to their admission offices for further information.

Then you can make good use of your summer vacations. Every year there are more student jobs available in science and new chances for study and experience in advanced science courses.

With support from the National Science Foundation, each summer several thousand students in all parts of the country are given training that will help them to decide on college programs and career plans. The Foundation supports between 100 and 200 secondary school programs for students of high ability, offering a variety of programs: training in astronomy and space science at the American Museum-Hayden Planetarium; advanced botany at the New York Botanic Garden; instruction in atmospheric science given by the American Meteorological Society; demonstrations, experiments, research and reports in various fields under the supervision of university faculties and visiting scientists; and many other unique courses and workshops.

Many similar programs are arranged by private schools, public school systems, industries and foundations in nearly every section of the country.

More hundreds of promising science students learn adult science in summer jobs in the laboratories of universities, industries and government agencies. Every summer more employers are offering such valuable experience to teen-agers. After some years of battling against age and formal training restrictions that kept them from such jobs, outstanding science students have proved to everyone's satisfaction that they can be extremely competent employees who are able to make important contributions.

If you are fortunate enough to get one of these jobs, you will find that you are given some real work to do instead of being confined simply to test tube washing and waste basket emptying. However, you will want to apply early (Christmas vacation might not be too soon to start), and to present all the recommendations, honors and other evidences of your ability in science that you have accumulated.

The experience gained in such jobs is invaluable, whether

you receive token payment or none at all. If, however, a modest salary happens to go along with the training, that is extra icing on the cake.

Three Giant Steps Toward Your Future

There are three exceedingly important and basic experiences that will take you a long way up the road toward becoming a scientist.

The first giant step is to see and experience for yourself, by one means or another, what a challenging adventure the pursuit of scientific truth can be.

The second is the personal discovery of the unforgettable thrill and incomparable satisfaction of finding and proving even a small bit of truth for yourself.

The third step is the process of building enough confidence in your own ability to believe that you can go on successfully searching and finding.

Perhaps the best means ever devised for accomplishing all three of these steps is the science project. A really good project can be an exciting challenge to your ingenuity, imagination, intuition and ability. You can find a problem so tantalizing that you carry it around in your mind, letting it simmer through whatever else you happen to be doing and thinking.

When you least expect it, you may have a sudden flash of insight. You can hardly wait then to try out the new idea. If your hunch is right, the pieces fall into place with brilliant clarity, and all at once you know what may have made Archimedes leap from his bath to rush into the street, shouting "Eureka!"

On the other hand, your hunch may be wrong or incomplete. The pieces scatter like mismatched bits of several jigsaw puzzles, and you search with considerable bewilderment for the pattern you thought you had glimpsed. When this happens, you pick up the sections that might conceivably fit and you start over—as many times as necessary.

Or, as sometimes happens, you may discover that your original insight is not new after all, that others have struggled better and longer with the same problem and have reported very solid solutions. Then you begin to think about it in a "what if" way to see if there are better answers or still unexplored tangents.

When you have developed and repeatedly tested your hypothesis and have organized all of your material, you have the basis for writing a report of your work. You may want to file your paper for future reference, or you may want to present it at a seminar, science congress or Junior Academy of Sciences meeting. You may want to submit it as part of a Science Talent Search entry, use it as part of an exhibit at a science fair or enter it in the Science Achievement Awards competition.

In Chapter 15 you will find complete information about Junior Academy of Sciences, Science Talent Search, science fairs, Science Achievement Awards and various other competitions. All of these can provide rewarding outlets for presenting projects, and may be of enormous help in your journey to a future in science.

The "Why" of Projects

Good ideas for science projects have come from every kind of source, ranging from a bad cold in the head to a bet that something couldn't be proved, from a newspaper report of the newest scientific development to a dream someone had one night. They have been sparked by a scientist's abstruse report on his research or one sentence in a scientific magazine.

Many a newspaper advertisement has set a fertile mind to wondering why or why not and what if, to thinking of ways a person might find out, and eventually to creating a project that investigated the whole business or some part of it.

Some projects are started for the pure fun of it. Their mainspring is usually that irresistible need to know or a yen to explore an especially exciting possibility. Some begin as rather boring homework required by a teacher for a passing grade in chemistry or extra credit in biology. It is interesting to note that when some of the National Science Fair finalists were asked what prompted them to create their projects in the first place, they made such honest confessions as, "My science teacher required that everyone do a project or fail the course"; "I had to have a science project to complete a credit in chemistry"; and, "The teacher got me in a corner, so I couldn't refuse him."

The greatest number of basic ideas for the 320 outstanding projects exhibited at the Tenth National Science Fair, held in Hartford, Connecticut, in May, 1959, were discovered in books, magazines, professional journals, newspapers, research papers, project lists and books (like this one) and even in science fiction. More than a third (thirty-five percent) of the National Science Fair finalists found their original inspiration in some kind of publication.

The ideas of twenty-eight percent of the finalists were developed from their own experiences, from experiments and projects they had been working on, from personal observation, curiosity, discussions and that sort of thing.

More than fourteen percent said suggestions for their projects came from school—from teachers and science club sponsors, school courses and laboratories.

Scientists, science clubs, fairs, institutes, laboratories, Junior Academies of Science or scientific equipment sparked the ideas of eleven percent.

Others mentioned sources such as science films, television science productions, slides, lectures, demonstrations, exhibits, etc. Several ideas came from summer jobs in scientific fields.

An astonishing assortment of investigations grew out of these ideas. For example, one finalist looked into the influence of carbohydrates upon the longevity of the adult wasp. Another worked on the theory, design and construction of a ten-and-a-half-inch cyclotron. There was a study of hormones in skunk cabbage, one on soap films, another on genetics and skin grafting.

It is interesting to see the kind of project that resulted from various idea sources. A representative sampling would be something like this:

Project Title	Source of Idea
"Gibberellic Acid—Plant Growth Stimulator"	conversation with neighbor
"Experimentation with Toxicology and Tranquilizers"	employment in drugstore
"Data-processing Computer"	newspaper article about Navy attempt to build a similar computer
"Bacterial Susceptibility to Antibiotics"	allergy to sulfa drugs
"Tissue Culture"	consultation with authorities at a U.S. Army hospital

"Study of the Rich Mountain Salamander"	suggestion of Junior Academy of Science sponsor
"Chemistry of Foam—A Solution to an Industrial Problem"	father's work
"Biochemical Aspects of Dentistry"	American Dental Association dental projects book
"Statistical Study of Finger Length Variation in the Adolescent Hand"	curiosity about difference in people's finger lengths
"The Effects of Radiation on the Blood in White Rats"	exhibit and discussion at science club
"The Braille-scriber, An Original Use for a Digital Computer"	discussion with instructors at school for the blind
"Physiochemical Basis of Memory"	article on memory in scientific magazine
"A Color Filter to Correct Color Blindness"	own color blindness

All of these are perfectly valid reasons for starting a science project. All have resulted in satisfying work that has, in addition, earned both praise and prizes.

Perhaps by now you are getting impatient to begin a project of your own. The rest of this book is designed to help you do that, whether this is your first project or merely the most advanced of a long series. Suggestions, directions, examples of successful project papers, illustrations, sources of information and equipment and hundreds of mind-stretching ideas have been assembled here to help you as much as possible.

The rest is up to you!

Chapter 2 • THE "HOW" OF PROJECTS

ALTHOUGH the best science projects seldom are created according to a recipe, there is an orderly series of steps that is followed pretty universally by successful students and professional scientists.

Seven Steps to a Successful Project

1. Decide on the specific problem or process you want to investigate.

2. Think it through, planning progressive steps, controls and checks in some detail. Try to foresee blind alleys before you become stalled in them. List unwanted factors that might influence your results and plan ways to prevent or make use of such accidents.

3. Read widely, since success with science projects depends largely on how much you know about your subject. Such reading will increase your understanding of the possibilities and limitations of your project and help you to see it in context. In addition to your school library, try the public libraries in your vicinity, and university, college and specialized libraries for books, journals, monographs and theses on your subject. When you have discovered relevant materials, dig into them deeply and take accurate notes, being sure to keep a complete record of your sources so you can give proper credit for borrowed material. If very little has been published in your field of investigation, at least you will know this and can include a statement to this effect in your project.

4. Talk to other people about your project and consult them about your plans. Often another student or an adult can

find a fuzzy area in your thinking, detect an error or suggest a method that will save you many hours of work or frustration. When you have gone as far as you can alone, professional scientists and technicians usually will be glad to help you over the rough spots. You will, of course, be considerate about querying them when they have time to answer, and only after you have done enough reading and thinking to be able to ask really intelligent questions. If you do not abuse their helpfulness, you may find adults eager to offer suggestions and even to lend you equipment, publications and other materials you might never discover for yourself. However, do *not* write an organization to send you everything it has on the subject, or expect the staff scientists to do your project for you.

5. Set up a notebook that will include accurate records of your original ideas, good and bad guesses, notes on your reading, all of your experiments and observations and graphs, tables, drawings, photographs or whatever is relevant and useful.

6. Begin the experiment or progressive steps of your project and establish the controls against which you will check each result. If the experiments do not yield the information you are looking for, record the results anyway and salvage whatever is useful in designing new experiments and controls. Remember that failures are instructive too. It often is extremely valuable to know what does not work.

7. Summarize your conclusions, when you have repeated your experiments sufficiently often to feel sure that your results are valid. Your conclusions may be positive or negative, since it is often as useful to prove a hypothesis false as true. If your work on this project opened up new questions that you hope to investigate, by all means mention these, too.

Writing a Report

Although there are many ways of writing about scientific work, the usual form for a written report is something like this:

1. Title—accurate, but not self-consciously long in an effort to impress

2. Summary—brief statement of the problem and the gist of your research

3. Introduction—reason for your interest in the problem, relevant work done by others, background information

4. Discussion of problem and hypothesis you are investigating

5. Details of materials, equipment, methods, steps of experiments, controls

6. Summary of observations and data

7. Conclusions drawn from observations

8. New questions, possible applications, future plans, if any

9. Appendix—graphs, tables, photographs, drawings

10. Bibliography and acknowledgements

Suggestions for Beginning Projects

If you are quite new at projects, obviously you won't want to undertake something like "Negative Ion Replacement as a Function of 'F' Centers in Alkali Metal Halides" (which was done by a member of the Honors Group of the Eighteenth Science Talent Search). To get the hang of it, try a simpler investigation that still allows a little room for originality, or do your own version of one of the classic experiments to see how scientific history was made.

Some of these might appeal to you or suggest others you would find especially interesting.

"An Electric Motor"
"Crystals and Crystal Forms"
"How the Telephone Works"
"Electroplating"
"Chemical Gardens"
"Uses of the Fulcrum"
"How Human Beings Perceive Depth"
"History of the Horse"
"The Stroboscope"
"Gravitational Laws"
"How Modern Mathematics Developed"
"Optical Illusions"
"Ben Franklin's Kite"

"Collections and Their Uses"
"Edison's Light Bulb"
"What Is in a Log?"
"The Effects of Weather on Man"
"Effects of Chemicals, Auxins, Light on Plants"
"Acid Production in the Mouth"
"Psychosomatic Medicine"
"Archimedes' Principle of Buoyancy"
"Exploring Fluorescence"
"How a Tooth Decays"

Directions for Beginning Projects

The following instructions came from material prepared for directors of science fairs affiliated with the National Science Fair-International, and for cooperating newspapers by Joseph H. Kraus, coordinator of the National Science Fair-International. These instructions will enable new student-scientists to begin work immediately on projects of their own.

An interesting project could be done by listing wild and cultivated plants that contain the milky substance called latex, collecting specimens of the plants, extracting the natural rubber, recording quantities obtained and experimenting with the sticky material.

The most important nontropical plant from which rubber is obtainable is guayule, but there are others which give latex, among them the desert milkweed, Indian hemp, goldenrod, some plants in the spurge family and some in the dogbane and nettle families. The common rubber plant, popular in the home, also will yield latex.

If you break off a leaf or small twig from a shrub or tree and see a milky white substance exuding from the break, you can assume that the sap contains rubber latex, particularly if it feels sticky to the touch. Make sure, however, that you avoid handling any of the growths toxic to the skin, like poison ivy or oak, or poison sumac.

While the cleanest sap will be obtained by the drip method, like that used in collecting latex from rubber trees, you may not have enough time to use this method. So uproot a number of specimens. Avoid crushing them until you get to your laboratory, then press out the juices by first cutting the stalks and then pressing them through a fruit press or a colander. Pass the liquid through a small piece of cheesecloth to free it of any foreign matter.

Measure the amount of liquid you have obtained. Dilute it with 2½ times as much water and stir. Add as much dilute acetic acid as you had original juice and observe the coagulation of the rubber latex. Milkweed is a good plant with which to try this experiment first.

Rubber latex can be purchased in small bottles, cans and tubes from art supply stores, garages and other places where it is sold for use as an adhesive and for making rubber molds.

Either this or the latex you get from plants may be used to illustrate the vulcanization process.

Stirring constantly, add latex slowly to about 25 times its volume of carbon tetrachloride, readily available from local stores under the trade name of Carbona. A colloid will form. To this slowly add about half as much powdered sulfur as you had latex, stirring constantly.

Place the mixture in a water bath (this operates on the same principle as the kitchen double boiler) and heat to the boiling point of water for about a half hour. If you have no water bath you can use a double boiler or place a small pot inside a larger one containing the hot water. Make sure the water doesn't boil out. Vulcanized rubber will be produced.

The hardness of the rubber depends on the quantity of sulfur added to it. The hardest rubber contains about thirty-two percent of chemically combined rubber. Many other substances may be added to it to modify its properties—catalysts, fillers, antioxidants and the like—and everything from huge conveyer belts and road surfaces to pillow stuffing and thin sewing machine thread can be made from rubber.

Two small mirrors, a piece of wood and a cardboard disk are all you need to make a range finder which will tell you the distance of a faraway object. Its precision will depend to some extent on the length of its base arm, but making and using even a small range finder will illustrate all the principles involved.

Mirrors for the range finders can be obtained from ladies' discarded compacts. Or you can cut a large broken mirror with a glass cutter into 2 pieces nearly alike, to measure about 1½ by 1 inch each. Try to get very thin glass mirrors to avoid double reflections. Or if you are familiar with the technique of making mirrors, make them from a couple of microscope slides, large cover glasses or, better yet, use surface-coated mirrors on optical flats.

Place a metal-edge ruler on the backing of one of the mirrors so that it divides the space in half horizontally. With a sharp razor blade cut through the backing and scrape off all the silver from half the glass. No such treatment is needed on the second mirror.

With a compass draw two identical circles on a piece of stiff cardboard. The diameter of these disks should be slightly longer than the length of your mirror. Cut out both disks. On one circle draw a line through the center, then draw two

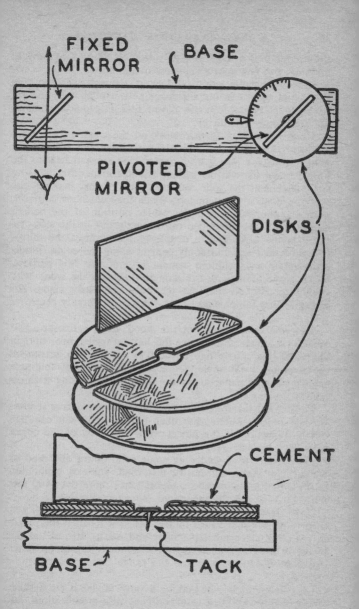

FIXED
MIRROR

BASE

PIVOTED
MIRROR

DISKS

CEMENT

BASE

TACK

lines parallel to it, one on each side. The total space between these lines should be the thickness of the mirror. In the center draw another circle, slightly larger in diameter than the head of a thumbtack. Cut out the space between the lines and cut out the inner circle. You now have a split disk to accommodate the tack head and mirror.

Before doing any further work on the disks, take a piece of wood about 3 inches wide, ½ inch thick and 1 foot long, and push a tack into it near one end. Remove the tack. The hole it has made will mark the position for the disk.

Now cement the split disk to the solid disk, making sure that the outside edges match. While the cement is still soft, push the thumbtack into the center position of the bottom circle. Stand the unscraped mirror vertically in the slot provided in the disk. Stick a couple of pins against the mirror to hold it in place and apply cement along the edges. Model airplane or any celluloid cement is good for this purpose. When the cement is dry, mount the disk on the wood with the thumbtack pushed into the hole previously made. Arrange a metal tab or other index marker, preferably bent over the edge of the disk, for indicating distances.

Near the opposite end of the wood, draw a line at a 45° angle to the edge and cement the half-scraped mirror upright along this line, mirror half upward. If you have no instrument for obtaining a 45° angle, you can do this easily by folding a square piece of paper along the diagonal and using it to establish the angle.

Look through the clear part of the stationary mirror at some vertical object. Rotate the other mirror until you can line up the reflection of the object with your view of the object through the clear area.

Place your range finder on some solid object and bind or weight it so that it will not be disturbed. For easy calibration select a position alongside a picket fence more than 100 feet long. Measure the distance from the range finder to a picket just 10 feet away. Spear a piece of paper on a picket, then return to your range finder, adjust it to align the picket in the clear glass and the mirror and mark "10 feet" at the place on the disk indicated by the pointer. Repeat for other distances. Now you can use the range finder holding it in your hand.

Once the principle of making a range finder is established, you probably will want to experiment with modifications. Instead of making your own disk you can use a radio dial or even the vernier control found in some radio sets. You may have to hacksaw a slot through the dial or file a slot through a cutoff condenser shaft to get your mirror properly held, but many a radio dial will allow for vernier precision and great accuracy of readings.

Then try a very long base line, about 6 feet or so, for establishing accuracy at greater distances. A knob at the sighting position connected by string to the rotating disk will make it easy to regulate the position of the mirror. But calibration should be made at the mirror circle because of stretch of the connecting cords which would defeat accurate reading at the control knob position.

To avoid reflections from the surrounding areas you can make the whole thing in a cardboard or metal tube, even reduce the size to make it very thin for photo purposes.

You can produce heat higher than 2000° F. with a simple electric furnace which you can build in an hour or so. You will need a cone-type porcelain wire-wound heater replacement element, available from hardware and supply stores. Also get a small bag of fiber asbestos or mica pellets, a pound of furnace cement, a small quantity of sand and two lugs similar to those on an electric iron or toaster. You also will need an 8-to-10-inch flowerpot, a heating appliance cord, a foot square of asbestos paper and a crucible cover or firebrick large enough to cover the top of the porcelain cone. You may also want a pyrometric cone for determining temperatures.

Leaving enough room for the appliance cord plug to fit under the rim of the flowerpot, drill two holes near the top of the pot, one under the other, to accommodate the lugs. Should you slip off a bit you can make repairs with the furnace cement. Insert the lugs and tighten the nuts with your fingers. Now attach the appliance cord connector to the lugs. Adjust the lugs until you are able to attach and remove the connector with reasonable ease. Now fill the hole in the bottom of the flowerpot with furnace cement and patch around the lugs if necessary.

With pliers break off the metal base of the heating element. A loop of string will keep the coil from sliding off the cone when the outside connection is freed. The string will burn off during the first heating. Place the heating element cone inside the pot, about ¼ of an inch below the rim. Pull the center wire from the top of the coil up over the top of

CRUCIBLE COVER

FLOWER-POT

MICA PELLETS

HEATING ELEMENT

REMOVE

the cone and twist it tightly around the upper lug nut with pliers or wrench. If it is not long enough to turn around the nut, stretch it by stealing a bit from the coils. Then attach the wire from the bottom end of the coil to the other lug.

If possible, test the continuity of the circuit with a lamp test. In a lamp test you take an electric cord and scrape the covering off each end of its two wires, leaving about one inch of bare wire at the ends. Attach a plug to the two wires at one end for plugging into an outlet later. Connect the other end of one of the wires to one side of a lamp socket. Attach a third wire to the other side of the lamp socket. Its ends should also be bared. Take the unattached end of this wire and the bare end of the electric cord wire and twist them around the two lugs on your furnace. Now attach the plug to an outlet. When a lamp is placed in the socket, it will light if your circuit has continuity. A faulty connection at the lugs, or a broken heating element, may give you a lot of trouble later, so now is the time to get it right.

For weight, throw an inch or so of the sand into the bottom of the pot, then add either the mica pellets or the dry asbestos fiber, packing in well to hold the wire cone in position. Continue to pack in the asbestos or mica until you have covered all of the resistance wires, but make sure in doing so that the two wires leading to the lugs are kept separated so that they will not short.

Plug the appliance cord into the circuit to see if the cone heats. Let it heat to redness and particularly watch for any sparking which may be due to moisture. If sparking occurs, disconnect immediately and let your furnace stand for a while before testing again. When you are sure everything is in order, cover the mica filling with a disk cut from the asbestos paper, with a hole at the center just large enough for a tight fit against the cone. You may have to slit from the edge to the hole to get the asbestos to fit the cone tightly.

Stuff a wad of paper or cloth into the cone to keep out the cement and top it with a crucible cover large enough to go over the cone. Better yet is a block cut from a furnace insulation firebrick. This is soft and can be cut easily with a handsaw. Now fill in the uncovered part of the top with furnace cement, smoothing with a trowel or flat knife. While the material is still soft remove the crucible cover or firebrick and mold the edges of the opening to give a finished surface. Test to make sure the cover fits back in place. Cracks may develop during drying, but these can be filled with cement. Do not hurry the drying operation by turning on the heat too soon.

All the material which is to be heated in the furnace should be put in small crucibles that will fit into the cone. Do not overload the crucibles and avoid spilling material on the inside of the cone, because it will be difficult to remove when hard.

If desired, a shelf can be raised inside the cone by leveling in some of the cement. From time to time this will have to be repaired because it will crack. Temperatures can be established through the use of pyrometric cones, which can be obtained from any dealer in ceramic supplies or pottery making equipment. In so small a unit temperatures achieved can be approximated by noting the amount of time required to reach a given level.

A more advanced project would be a larger electric furnace for high temperatures. Temperatures of more than 2000° F. can be reached in this furnace in less than 2 hours from a cold start. Suited to any experiments dealing with melting ores, metals, metallurgical testing, sintering, heat treatment, reduction, oxidation, determination of ash content, enamels, glazes or any of the many others demanding high heat, this furnace will be found to prove most satisfactory at a cost of less than $10.00, involving work easily done in a single day.

For its construction you will need a case (25) of insulation firebricks; about 10 pounds of high refractory cement; 2 nichrome wire replacement resistors, either 600 watts or, preferably, 1000 watts each; 4 steel studs, ¼ inch in diameter, 6 inches long and threaded at both ends; 8 nuts and steel washers to fit; 2 snap switches; 4 iron wood screws, 3¼ inches long; connecting wire; and pyrometric cones to determine temperature.

Plunge six bricks into a pail of water, one at a time, and remove almost immediately. Do not let bricks soak up too much water or it will take several weeks of drying before you can put the furnace into operation. These bricks will form the base of the furnace. Set the bricks side by side on a newspaper-covered level surface and cement them together with a thin, even layer of cement.

Place two dry bricks on each side of the furnace and fill in the back with cut bricks. The front will be formed by

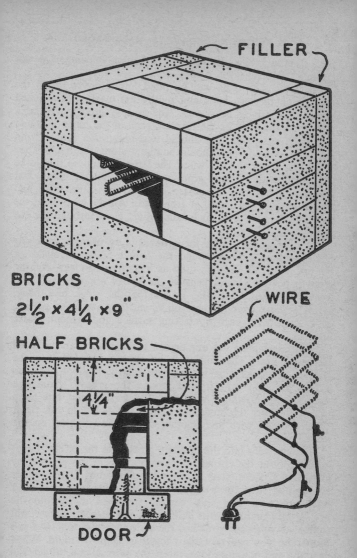

FILLER

BRICKS
2½" × 4¼" × 9"

HALF BRICKS

4¼"

WIRE

DOOR

base, top and side bricks, with a center opening. Do not cement the bricks yet.

The resistance coils will be fitted into grooves inside the furnace on the left, back and right. First mark with a pencil where they are to be placed. The bottom groove will be 1 inch from the floor of the furnace; each of the other 3 should be 1 inch apart. Grooves should start about 2½ inches from the front opening and should continue along the back. They should be about ¼ inch wide. The left-side grooves should be connected with vertical grooves in the following way: first and second grooves connected at front ends, also third and fourth grooves connected at front ends. All the grooves at the right should have a ¼-inch hole drilled clear through for the steel studs.

An easy way to make the grooves is by using a hack-saw blade held in a wrap-around rag handle. A small chisel or the end of a file may be used as a scraper to clean out the grooves but be careful because the bricks are very soft and easily damaged. Wet the bricks for the sides and back, sprinkle water over the area on which they are to be placed, apply cement to each contacting surface and cement bricks together.

With pliers bend out one or two loops at each end of each resistance coil. The coils can be stretched to fit into the grooves. To determine what length each coil should be, run a piece of light rope in and around the grooves from one stud hole to another. Now thread a washer and nut on a stud and insert the stud into one of the holes on the right. Then add the wire and another washer and tighten on the second nut.

Slide the wire into the first two grooves in the bricks, bending sharply at the corners. Secure the wire in the grooves by long iron U tacks, steel hairpins or, preferably, U pins made by bending strips of wire cut from a broken and discarded resistance coil. The coils can be stretched to fit into the bricks, but guard against shifting. A pin at each corner will suffice. If you have stretched the resistance coil too far for a proper fit, you can squeeze it together again by hand. When near the end of the groove, insert the second stud, attach the other end of the coil to it and add a washer and nut. Repeat this process with the other coil and the other two studs. Now use a lamp test to check the continuity of both circuits.

Wet six bricks to form the top of the furnace and cement them in place, then cement in filler pieces from cut bricks.

Split a brick lengthwise by sawing across its 4¼-inch face and cut each piece for a snug fit into the front opening. An old saw will cut through the bricks as if they were softest wood. Center these two pieces on two full bricks set flat side by side and mark latter only for drilling holes to accommodate freely the iron screws. Wet bricks, apply cement to all facing surfaces and screw together, driving screw heads below the surface. Fill the holes with cement and wipe off any surplus cement from around the edges.

Allow several days to dry. Connect studs with wires and switches, but be careful to avoid turning the studs or you may disturb connections inside. Turn on the current and watch inside. If sparking occurs between the wire and the walls, disconnect and let the furnace dry for several days more.

When ready to test, drill a 1-inch-diameter peephole through the middle of the door. Cut a plug from a piece of firebrick to fit the hole. A file will shape it quickly, or you can use coarse sandpaper. Put a pyrometric cone into a small lump of clay to hold it on a slant, then press the clay onto a length of firebrick cut so that the cone can be seen through the opening. Heat the furnace until the cone melts. Allow the furnace to cool slowly the first few times.

If this furnace is exhibited at a fair, it should not be maintained in operation unless the exhibitor can equip it with an automatic cutoff. The heat developed is great enough to melt the resistance wires or severely oxidize the coils. Properly handled, however, the furnace will last a long time. If elements need replacing, the job can be done quickly and inexpensively.

Building Equipment and Using It

Although a piece of equipment or a scientific instrument you have built makes a good exhibit for a science fair, the real test is not so much the building of the equipment as what you do with it after you have made it. You may want to start simply by building, but you should go on to use the equipment in an investigation, and then to still more extensive and advanced studies.

Improvising

Some projects give the impression of having cost a great deal or of requiring equipment totally beyond the reach of the average student. But in most instances these projects are dramatic examples of what can be done with imagination, resourcefulness and rather unlikely junk.

It is surprising how many motors from old washing machines, electric fans and similar items have gone through forcible metamorphosis and emerged as scientific equipment. Surplus electronic supplies, such as tubes, wiring, switches, etc., have been bought very inexpensively by many projecteers, who also report that they have discovered all kinds of potentially useful bits and pieces for sale in junk yards or about to be disposed of as scrap by industrial organizations.

One project at the Tenth National Science Fair, an ingenious push-button telephone dial system, was constructed from scrap iron, aluminum shutters salvaged from a junk yard, scrap wire from the telephone company and relays found in a junk yard and successfully cleaned up.

The springs from fifty ball-point pens were used in building a computer to solve quadratic equations.

Such items as a tape recorder, Christmas tree lights, old television parts and a rotating flasher were used to build a robot. Incidentally, this was a very accomplished, electronically controlled robot, which talked, moved around and picked up objects by remote control. It also boasted a rotating antenna and a halo that lit up when it was especially well behaved.

If a tour of the attic and basement, local surplus equipment suppliers, junk yards and industrial scrap heaps doesn't turn up usable material, try some of the mail-order companies that specialize in items of this sort. Some are listed in Chapter 16, and many advertise in newspapers and magazines.

Projects for Everyone

In the following chapters you will find descriptions of projects in almost every area of science. You can read through them all, or simply look at those that especially interest you. With the exception of some cutting here and there, these papers are presented just as the students have written them.

Sometimes the papers refer to illustrations and diagrams which do not appear in the book; mention of these has been included to give you an idea of the scope of the projects and the way in which they were reported.

These papers represent varying levels of scientific sophistication and are offered as examples of how some projects have been reported. But they are not models to be copied in detail, for there are many right ways to describe a project, and you will, of course, want to plan yours to fit your own procedures and results.

1

Joanne Zerger, Salina, Kansas, presented her project, "Showing Phosphorus Uptake by Autoradiography," at the Ninth National Science Fair.

"Finding uses for radioactive isotopes as tracer elements is one of the newest fields in which research is being done today. It is an extremely important field, and I have certainly found it to be one of the most interesting.

These radioisotopes, as they are sometimes called, are becoming more and more extensively used in industry, as well as in various areas of physical and biological science. When they are used as tracer elements they become the key that unlocks some of the fascinating secrets of nature. Much valuable data has been discovered and many important hypotheses confirmed by this method.

The project I exhibited at this year's National Science Fair illustrated with X rays the way a plant absorbs nutrients, namely phosphorus, from the soil. I used a method of measuring radioactivity which we call autoradiography. This method will measure radioactivity without a Geiger counter and also produces a permanent record. Following is a summary of what I did and the materials I used.

I first tried growing the young tomato plants I needed for my project, but as they were out of season I had considerable difficulty. I finally was able to obtain some of the right size, about six inches tall, from a greenhouse. Any small plant would have sufficed, but I chose them because their leafiness made them show up best on an X ray.

I soaked the soil off the roots of the plants, being careful not to injure or destroy the very fine roots and thus decrease the absorbing power.

Then I prepared a solution in a 150-ml. beaker. To 100-ml. of distilled water I added 10 microcuries of radioactive phosphorus (P^{32}). I ordered it from the Abbott Laboratories in Oak Ridge, Tennessee, and this was the largest generally licensed quantity I could obtain. This phosphorus had a half life of 14.3 days, so I could not order it too far in advance. It was in compound form, disodium phosphate. I added 1 gm. of stable disodium phosphate to the radioactive sample to act as a carrier for the P^{32}. Also added were a few drops of concentrated nitric acid to aid diffusion of the solution into the plant.

Next I placed the roots of eight clean plants into the solution. I removed one plant after thirty minutes of time had elapsed and one at the end of every following thirty-minute period. As there were eight plants, the last one was in the solution four hours. After I removed each plant from the solution, I proceeded with the autoradiograph.

The autoradiographs were prepared in the following way. The roots of the plants were cut off, because they were so soaked with solution I was afraid they would severely over-expose the film. I then placed the plant on some Saran Wrap, flattened it out and arranged the leaves so they didn't overlap and wrapped it up to prevent the plant from coming in direct contact with the film. This package was placed directly on the film. This film was regular medical X-ray film, five inches by seven inches. Then the film and wrapped tomato plant were placed in a previously constructed folder. I made this folder from lightweight cardboard wrapped with black construction paper. After closing the folder I placed it between two layers of spongy padding and put several heavy books on top of this. When all eight folders were filled, I left them unmoved in total darkness for four days. The length of time that the folders are left, exposing the film to the radioactive phosphorus absorbed by the plant, would vary directly with the age of the P^{32}, because it disintegrates as time goes on. The length of time has to be determined by trial and error.

When you think the film has been sufficiently exposed by the P^{32} to make a clear print on the film, develop one of them and see. It is better to use one of the films from a plant that was in the solution for a relatively long time, because some of the earliest ones will not make more than a few faint streaks, even when sufficiently exposed, because the plant behind them did not absorb very much P^{32}. For this test it would be advisable to have two films, one on either side of the plant in some of the later folders, so if the test proves that more time is needed there will still be one left that will be sufficiently exposed.

To develop the film I placed it in some X-ray developer

solution for about five minutes, or until it seemed that it was developed as well as possible. Then I rinsed it in some X-ray fixer solutions for about ten minutes. I then thoroughly washed the X-ray film. During the time the film was in the solutions I kept it moving. This developing procedure, of course, had to be done in a darkroom.

These X-ray films, when developed and placed in order, showed a steady progression from a faint streak in the region of the lower stem to a sharp print of the entire plant.

These are the conclusions I drew from this project.

Tracer elements are a very good practical way of discovering and collecting data of scientific importance.

The tagged element phosphorus in the isotope 32 makes an efficient tracer element.

The nutrient phosphorus is translocated from the roots to the stems and finally to the leaves of plants in a relatively short time.

The absorption of phosphorus varies directly with the time the roots are in contact with it. This absorption seems to take place more rapidly than I had supposed.

This completed my actual project but I did additional reading on radioisotopes; their applications, including their use as tracer elements; the various areas of research in which tracer elements are being used; and any other information that might help me to know more about the general field.

Some of the additional information pertaining directly to my project was on the exhibit, along with some very brief diagrams of my procedure. I had displayed my eight autoradiographs and a sample folder with the film ready to be exposed.

My total expenses, excluding paper and ink for displaying the project, were only $4.50.

I feel that I have learned a great deal from this project, even though it was on a small scale. My work with radioisotopes, especially their use as tracer elements, is in a new field of study and research. This field, I am sure, has extremely great potentialities and will contribute much toward the betterment of modern man."

2

Richard Burger of Jamaica, New York, one of the forty

winners in the Seventeenth Science Talent Search for the Westinghouse Science Scholarships and Awards conducted by Science Clubs of America, an activity of Science Service, did an outstanding study of sundews, "A Time Lapse Photographic Study of the Reaction of *Drosera intermedia* to Certain Chemical and Physical Stimuli." Quoted here are part of the Introduction; Section 2 (Techniques), Part A (Culturing); part of Section 3 (Observations and Film Notes); and Section 4 (Summary of Observations, Conclusions and Suggestions for Further Experimentation).

"Every biology student has seen pictures and read of the sundews *(Drosera)*, a small genus of insectivorous plants which possess the power to engulf small insects with their several dozen tentacles. This unusual ability has made them an object of intense study ever since Darwin's *Insectivorous Plants*. One of the problems presented by these plants is the nature of the stimuli to which they react. The insect, their natural stimulator, presents three stimuli. This paper is devoted to a study of each of these stimuli taken separately to determine their respective parts in the plant's total reaction.

Sundews are quite common in their natural habitat, bogs and pine barrens. Their choice of habitat is responsible for the general public's lack of familiarity with this plant. Anyone who can tolerate wet feet can enjoy a profitable collecting expedition. My collections were made at Mud Pond (in Sullivan County, New York), a bog which I had visited regularly since 1952. The plants grow in several zones from the innermost portion of the marginal mat back into the spaces between the honeysuckle, blueberry and bog spruce which make up the ecologically oldest portion of the bog. Other bogs in the area which I found to contain such plants are shown on the map on page 10. Of the three main species of sundew, *D. filiformis, D. intermedia* and *D. rotundifolia*, the latter two are present in this bog. *D. intermedia* is confined to the innermost portion of the mat.

Culturing

In the course of several trips I found it most effective to uproot colonies of plants and surrounding sphagnum moss, placing several in a plastic bag. Although such handling nullified the trapping ability of the present leaves, it kept the plants moist. They were transplanted to a glass-covered terrarium, exposed for about eight hours a day to direct sunlight and within a week new leaves had replaced the old, new buds appearing at the rate of one a day for several months.

It appeared that the health and vigor of the plant were best reflected in the amount of red in the glands and tentacles. Specimens of *D. rotundifolia*, which had lost all red through the winter, and of *D. intermedia*, which had only faintly colored marginal glands, were placed near a large window and kept lighted constantly with an electric light bulb. Within a month the color had returned to all glands and the size of the leaves had doubled from 3/16″ to 3/8″ in the largest dimension. Observations in the bog corroborated the conclusion that the amount of light received by the leaf was responsible for the development of vigorous glands. Sundews growing among the roots of trees (*D. rotundifolia*) constantly showed less red than those growing in clearings, and these in turn were paler than those growing on open mud (*D. intermedia*). On identical amounts of light, *D. intermedia* was able to maintain its health better, as indicated by the previously stated rule of thumb, and confirmed this theory when tested with meat. For this reason, *D. intermedia* was chosen for study.

Observations

My observations are summarized in 54 feet of time-lapse movies culled from over 200 feet exposed and studied. In scenes one and two, leaves are stimulated by meat; in scene three by glass; in scenes four and five, leaves are briefly touched by a copper wire; in scenes six and seven, casein is dusted on the leaves. Important or unusual phenomena are noted below. . . .

Conclusions

In most cases, the reaction to touch was faster than that to meat, although the former never achieved completion. In the experiments conducted with glass, the reaction up to the freeze phase was approximately as violent as the control. The reaction to casein was, in turn, still slower, and the leaf on the whole did not approach the inflection caused by glass. The slight reaction was a complete one in that the leaf remained partly inflected for several days, presumably until the proteins had been digested.

From these observations, two tentative conclusions are drawn:

1) Protein is necessary if the reaction is to be complete.

2) The intensity of unit pressure on the tentacles is responsible for the speed of reaction. This raises a question: Is casein dust really the pure chemical stimulus it was assumed to be? Could a fine glass dust elicit a comparable incomplete reaction? If the answer to the latter question is affirmative, and hence, the former's answer negative, the casein dust reaction could be assumed to be a manifestation of the two tentative conclusions. However, to verify this, it must follow that a pure chemical reaction be observed. At the present time, I am trying to devise a way in which a stimulus, completely devoid of mechanical components or at least below the sundew's reception level, can be applied.

An unexpected effect observed was that the plant, when stimulated physically only, would close fairly rapidly to a certain point, then suddenly freeze, and remain immobile for about two hours. Next, relaxation of the tentacles, then the leaf blade, slowly becomes obvious. It seems possible that this pause takes place in lieu of the transition to the chemical stimulus supposed responsible for the reaction's completion. I hope that closer observation of this and similar phases may shed light on the relationships of the two stimuli on the total reaction."

3

Thomas Mike Church of Fort Wayne, Indiana, was a finalist in the Ninth National Science Fair. His project was "Effects of Light Variation on Plant Growth."

"Light

The machine is divided into four identical compartments, each painted white for maximum efficiency and reflection of all wavelengths. See Fig. 2.

In the intensity experiment, four tungsten light bulbs of 25-50-75-100 wattages were used. (Fig. 3) Theoretically emission from these light bulbs at the distance of the plants in this experiment should be 162.5—325—478.6—650 lux; but light-meter readings at the appropriate positions showed 56—160—224—300 foot-candles, or 601.724—1722.24—2372.136—3229.2 lux. This is explained by reflection from the white surfaces and variation in manufacture of the bulbs. The later readings in lux are equivalent to 3.00892—8.6112 —11.86068—16.146 x 10^3 ergs/cm.^{2}/sec. visible radiation.

Spectrographs of the bulbs were taken. Visible emission is shown in Table A. There was no difference that would affect growth very perceptibly. Of course, a greater variation was present in the infrared portion of the spectrum; but the effect of infrared rays on photosynthesis is largely and perhaps completely the production of heat.

In the photoperiodism experiment, 75W bulbs were used. Emission was 200 foot-candles, 2152.8 lux or 10.761 10^2 ergs/cm.^{2}/sec. Spectrum similar to 75W bulb in Table A.

Temperature

The fact that the chambers are white helps to prevent the absorption of infrared rays (consequently preventing heat accumulation). The compartments containing the light sources are isolated from the plants by sealed panes of glass (Fig. 4); and adjustable ventilating louvers are placed in the back as additional precautions. (Fig. 2) A blower is attached to the back of one chamber to cool a light source which might develop considerable heat otherwise. (A blower from an old oil furnace proved satisfactory.)

Thermometers were placed in each compartment to monitor the temperature. Variations were corrected by adjusting the louvers. (Generally, too much heat was the problem. Obviously, if the temperature of the air surrounding the machine is high, then the temperature of the box will not drop very quickly when desirable. A cellar is a good place to locate the machine.)

Available Water in Soil

To test the water content of the soil in each box of plants, I built the meter-equipped device in Fig. 1 (bottom center). It is on the order of an ammeter, but more greatly specialized; it permits a side-by-side comparison of the water content in each box of soil through a switching device, without the use of movable probes or having to record numbers. It contains a transistor amplifier stage, and applies 22½ V.D.C. to the soil probes. These brass probes are arranged at equal distances (eight inches) and identical positions and depths in each compartment. A basic schema is shown in Fig. 5.

Figure 5 — SCHEMA OF SOIL TESTER

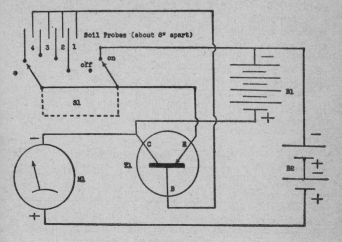

PARTS LIST

- **S1** — 5PST nonshorting switch with on-off switch coupled

T1 — CK768 transistor

M1 — 5 ma Meter (DC)

B1 — 22½V. transistor battery

B2 — 3V. battery (2 size "D" flashlight cells in series)

Soil Probes — nonferrous, e.g., brass. Insert almost to bottom of boxes. (Note: Do **not** use metal boxes.)

Other Factors

Humidity was considered to be essentially equal (i.e., since the temperature and water were equal, the rate of evaporation and hence the humidity should have been equal). Air circulation was identical, as far as it would influence the growth rate. Since the available air came from the same source, the immediate area surrounding the box, the CO_2, O, and other gas compositions were regarded as being the same. Soil composition was identical. Plants were all germinated at the same time and removed from illumination at the same time. Sufficient time after germination was allowed for expension of the nourishment in the seed.

Preliminary Experimentation

Oats and corn were run for two weeks in the machine; results on height showed that more temperature correction was necessary (ventilating louvers and a blower devised). I also concluded that a shorter time under illumination should be used, since under the higher illumination conditions, the plants showed signs of withering in the constant light. Four or five days proved to be sufficient (oats sprout in a week, grow to nine inches in two weeks).

Results of measurements not worth mentioning, since most of growth was caused by heat differences and evaporation of water (humidity increase).

Measurement of Photosynthetic Activity

To determine relative photosynthetic activity, I used the dry weight of the plants. The plants were dehydrated in a vacuum at 140° F. for about an hour. (They were weighed periodically during this time; when there was no more drop in weight, it was assumed that all the water had been removed.) [Note: Many industrial laboratories, e.g., General Electric, have the facilities and would be willing to assist in this operation.]

Weights were taken before and after dehydration in two parts: the weight of the major portion of the green stem and of the root system. The graphs show the weight of the entire plant, instead of just the part where photosynthesis took place, because of transmigration of plant substances between the leaves and the roots.

While there are, naturally, more efficient methods of measuring photosynthetic activity (including gas exchange, oxygen-bubble counting, etc.), the method utilized here is perhaps the simplest and most convenient. It was possible because the plants were of the same species, the same age and their influencing factors, other than the one being observed, equal. Of course, the hypothesis here is that an increase in the photosynthetic rate produces a proportional increase in the dry weight of the plant.

First Experiment: Intensity of Illumination

Newly sprouted oats, all ½" high, were placed in the machine for the experiment. Temperature throughout the duration of the experiment remained constant at 70° F. in all boxes. Water was checked frequently (every two hours during the day) with the meter.

The relative heights of the plants in each box at different stages in the experiment are shown in Table B. The box numbers at the bottom correspond to those in Fig. 4. It can be clearly seen that the height of a plant does not increase directly with the intensity of illumination, and possibly has very little relation to it. From #2 we can observe that if the duration of the experiment were extended, the greatest height would probably be obtained at an intermediate intensity. It seems that plants exposed to high and low levels of light (#1, #4) will attain approximately equal heights, the former having no need to attain height in order to receive light, and the latter in an attempt to come closer to the source of light.

It is also interesting to note that #2, the plant which would eventually attain the greatest height, shows the greatest loss of weight during dehydration (Table C). But #1, which did not attain a great height but had the greatest rate of photosynthesis, shows the lowest loss, because of its larger per-volume dry-matter content; and this was a result of the higher rate of photosynthesis. It can also be seen that the higher intensities of illumination, and the resulting greater rates of photosynthesis, had little or no relation to the stem/root weight ratio, or even the stem/root dry-matter concentration ratio, from observation of the two similar graphs in Table C.

The relative rates of photosynthesis (i.e., the dry weights) are represented in Table D. From observation of the scale, it can be seen that there is about a 4% increase in dry weight for every 100% increase in light intensity, under the conditions in the experiment. As is also evident, however, the highest intensity in the experiment is still less than the intensity of full sunlight; and while there is probably an increase in photosynthesis up to sunlight, intensities much greater would be likely to destroy the photosynthetic mechanism.

A comparison with the results of Mitchell and Rosendahl, 1939, who also used dry weights to determine photosynthetic activity in relation to light intensity, is shown in Table E.

Second Experiment: Photoperiodism—the
Time-Phase Generator (or Interrupter)

I constructed this contrivance (Fig. 6) to provide the necessary intermittent light for the experiment. I favored it over the method used by Warburg (rotating sectors) because it was more practical in my case. The interrupter apportions light to the plants in the following manner:

Box 1——On constantly
Box 2——On .5 seconds, off .5 seconds
Box 3——On 3 minutes 40 seconds,
    off 10 minutes 11 seconds
Box 4——On 7 minutes 54 seconds,
    off 5 minutes 57 seconds

If the effect of the intermittent light could be disregarded, day-lengths would be:

1——24 hours
2——12 hours
3——5.19 hours
4——12.815 hours

Referring again to Fig. 6, it is clearly seen that this is no professional instrument. But the object of my experiment was to construct a workable machine in a minimum of time, and to devote most of my energies to more important phases of the experiment, not to build a beautiful, ultra-precision instrument. Nevertheless, it is versatile; it has quite a large current-carrying capacity; has readily adjustable time periods; took little time to build; is constructed mainly of spare parts, which made it quite cheap; and is precise enough for most uses one would want to apply it to.

Discussion, General Conclusions
of Photoperiodism Experiment

The continuous light in Box 1, the control, was considered simply on the basis of equal time, not equal period of illumination with the other boxes. Therefore, while it appears to be fairly close to #2 and #4 in Table G (rate of photosynthesis), it really is only a little more than 50% of them if equal periods of illumination are considered. An explanation of this might be that during the dark periods carbon dioxide would have an opportunity to enter the centers of photosynthetic activity and synthesized material to move away, both of which would tend to increase the rate of photosynthesis.

In Table F, the heights of the plants at different stages in the experiment are represented. Comparing #3, in Table F and Table G, it can be seen that, while it has the lowest height of any of the plants in the experiment, it also had the greatest rate of photosynthesis. An increase in dark time over light time in the early stages of plant growth seems to produce a marked increase in the photosynthetic rate.

(Incidentally, the plants increased in height during the second twenty-four hours three times as much as they did during the first twenty-four hours.)

I plan to experiment with longer growth periods and wider ranges of photoperiodism, as well as with longer growth ranges and wider ranges of intensities of light.

Bibliography

Plant Physiology, Meyer and Anderson
Photosynthesis, Spoehr
Introduction to Plant Physiology, Curtis and Clark
Photosynthesis, Hill and Cunningham
Plant Physiology, Levitt
(Technical Paper) "Responses of Spring Wheat Varieties to Day-Length at Different Temperatures," Gries, Stearns, Caldwell

Acknowledgments

Mr. R. V. Huffman (GE), for his help in dehydrating the plants
Mr. R. C. Weber and Mr. Don Weaver, my sponsors

Miss M. Davenport, for her help in making the signs for exhibition

Mr. R. M. Caldwell, Prof. of Botany, Purdue University

Mr. John C. Torrey, Associate Prof. of Botany, University of California"

4

Karen Reynolds of Marysville, California, exhibited her project at the Ninth National Science Fair. She investigated the "Environmental Effects on Plants of the Sutter Buttes." A summary of her study follows.

"The character of plant life is the result of environmental conditions due to soil, water, temperature, wind, sunlight, animals and the like. The result of a curiosity as to how plants responded to their environments was a study of the variation in plant growth on the Sutter Buttes, called the smallest mountain range in the world, located about sixty-five miles north-northwest of Sacramento, California.

Using South Butte (elevation 2117 ft.) as the field of study, I examined plants of the same species in their different environments. The mountain was divided into "base" (200-800 ft.), "middle" (800-1400 ft.) and "top" (1400-2100 ft.), as well as into "north slope" and "south slope." Some of the basic facts on the effects on plant distribution discovered were as follows:

1. Soil becomes progressively less fertile in the advance up the slope due to weathering by wind and water, which carry fertile topsoil downward and deposit it at the base.

2. Less water is to be found in the soil at higher altitudes, for moisture-holding factors are lacking.

3. The length of the root in proportion to the rest of the plant increases as the soil varies from moist fertile humus to dry clay or rocky soil.

4. Numerous rocks are an obstruction to plant growth, but also serve to hold soil in place.

5. Prevailing winter winds come from the south while dry summer breezes come from the north.

6. Plants on the south slope are of the small varieties except in sheltered ravines, where larger plants are able to grow.

7. Plants growing on the sheltered north slope are greater

in variety, including larger shrubs, bushes and trees, which dominate the north slope and are scarce on the south.

8. The peak of the mountain "catches" low clouds and often becomes surrounded by fog.

9. Due to the sun's rays' hitting more directly on the south slope than on the north slope, the south side is generally warmer than the north.

10. Grazing animals help to fertilize the soil and are the cause of short grass on the slopes.

This study was explained in an exhibit by use of a scale model of the Buttes and of South Butte made of paper and flour-water paste; soil samples taken from various locations on South Butte; numerous plants collected from the slopes of South Butte, pressed and mounted; and written identifications and explanations. The total cost was about twenty-five dollars, while the value of the experience and knowledge gained is ten times the cost and more."

5

A love of flowers led Patricia Van de Vyver, Detroit, Michigan, to a study of natural pigments. Her project, which was presented at the Tenth National Science Fair, is described below.

"Introduction

Though simple in outward appearance, plants are complex organisms.

In my project, "Natural Pigments," I have attempted to extract and separate the pigments found in the leaves and flower petals of different plants.

The separation procedure was carried out by three different methods:
(a) immiscible solvents
(b) column chromatography
(c) circular paper chromatography

Each of these methods was used independently of the others.

Pigments

The plastid and vacuolar pigments found in plants can be

classified into three divisions according to solubility: the pigments which are soluble in water, the ones which are soluble in petroleum ether and the ones which are soluble in alcohol.

The water-soluble pigments, which are found in the vacuolar sap of plants, are:

(a) the anthocyanins (red, blue, purple), and

(b) the anthoxanthins (yellow). The anthoxanthins are not as conspicuous as the anthocyanins, but they are found together with them in the flower heads.

The most common plastid pigments occurring in the leaves of higher plants are:

(a) the alpha-chlorophyll (blue-green), the beta-chlorophyll (yellow-green) and the carotenes (orange). These are all soluble in petroleum ether and in carbon disulfide.

(b) the xanthophylls (yellow), which are soluble in alcohol and also in carbon disulfide.

Extraction of Pigments

In the extraction process, the leaves or flowers were cut into small pieces (1 or .5 cm. sq.), placed in a mortar that contained a little sand and about 70 cc. of isopropyl alcohol and ground thoroughly until the pigments were extracted.

In the case of the leaves, a little petroleum ether was used to further complete the extraction of the chlorophylls.

Separation of Pigments
A. Method of Immiscible Solvents

Since the petals or leaves of plants are composed of various types of pigments (those soluble in water, alcohol or petroleum ether), these types can be separated from one another.

In the flower petals, the anthocyanins and anthoxanthins which are soluble in water were separated from the carotenes and xanthophylls which are soluble in carbon disulfide. Equal amounts of carbon disulfide and the alcohol-water solution of the pigments were mixed together. The xanthophylls and carotenes separated out with the carbon disulfide, while the water-soluble pigments remained in the alcohol-water solution.

In separating the pigments of the leaf, petroleum ether was used with the alcohol solution of the leaf pigments. In this case, the carotenes and chlorophylls which are soluble in petroleum ether were separated from the xanthophylls which are soluble in alcohol.

B. Column Chromatography

A valuable technique used in scientific research and in technology is column chromatography. This method is used to separate complex mixtures into their individual components. In applying this technique to the separation of the leaf pigments, and of the pigments in the flower heads, the materials that I used and the results I obtained differed slightly, but the basic principles remained the same.

For the chromatograms, I used a piece of glass tubing having an outside diameter of 10 mm. and a length of 16 inches. About one inch of ordinary absorbent cotton was packed loosely at one end. The absorbing material was introduced at the other end of the tubing under suction, using small portions and packing down each portion with a glass rod.

At first, I experimented with finely powdered calcium carbonate, magnesium carbonate and aluminum oxide as materials for the column. I found that these powders were quite satisfactory for separating the leaf pigments, but not satisfactory at all for separating the water-soluble pigments extracted from the flower heads, since they reacted readily with these pigments. After further experimentation with starch, powdered sugar and powdered cellulose, I decided to use the powdered cellulose as the most suitable absorbent for the column. Being inactive, cellulose did not react with the pigments; it had fairly good absorbing qualities, and the chromatogram took only about six hours to run to completion.

The column was filled to a height of about ten inches. After this, the solvent was carefully introduced under suction, and time was allowed for the column to become thoroughly wet with the solvent. The solvent I found best for the water-soluble pigments was a water-saturated butanol-acetic acid mixture. To make this mixture, I used 20 ml. of butanol, 5 ml. of glacial acetic acid and 25 ml. of water. The organic phase was carefully drawn off and used to wet the column in preparation for the chromatography of the flower pigments.

For the chromatography of the leaf pigments, I used a mixture of 22.5 ml. of petroleum ether, 2.5 ml. of acetone and .5 ml. of benzene, since the leaf pigments proved to be insoluble in the butanol-acetic acid mixture.

The plant extract to be analyzed was in the meantime allowed to dry thoroughly and was then dissolved in 3 cc. of the same solvent that was used for the column. It was then poured on top of the prepared column and allowed to enter the cellulose. The pigments immediately began to show zones of adsorption on the column. To develop these zones further, fresh solvent was poured into the tube and allowed to percolate downward. Soon distinct colored bands began to form on the cellulose.

The pigments were separated into bands because of a difference in adsorption coefficients of these components on the column of the adsorbent. The components which are least readily adsorbed will tend to run down the column while the others lag behind. Also those that are more soluble in the solvent will move downward faster than those that are less soluble.

The four main bands that I found to form on the chromatogram of the leaf pigments were the alpha-chlorophyll, the beta-chlorophyll and the carotenes. On the flower chromatogram, the bands formed were those of the different anthoxanthins, anthocyanins and xanthophylls.

C. Circular Paper Chromatography

I also attempted a separation of the plant pigments from the leaves and the flower heads by the more recent method of paper chromatography. This method utilizes the principle that a solution containing a mixture of substances can be resolved into its components by virtue of their different degrees of absorption on filter paper.

I first experimented with strip chromatography, which is the conventional method. While doing research on chromatographic technique, I came upon an article describing circular paper chromatography. I decided to give this method a trial and found that it gave more satisfactory results than the strip method. I decided to use it for the separation of my plant pigments.

The following description explains the apparatus and the method I used. A circular sheet of Whatman's No. 1 filter paper, about 10 inches in diameter, was placed between the plane ground surfaces of 2 equal-sized plates of glass about 7 mm. thick. The upper glass plate had a circular hole in its center with a diameter of 6 mm. The solution of the pigments to be analyzed was applied through this hole with a capillary tube and the resulting spot was allowed to dry. The nozzle of a standard 10-ml. pipette was then fitted into the hole and the pipette was charged with solvent. The solvent used was the same as described previously for the column chromatography of the leaf and the flower pigments respectively.

The speed of effluence of the solvent was automatically controlled by the absorbing power of the paper and could be regulated by adjusting the pressure of the nozzle against the paper. As the solvent front advanced in a slowly widening ring, it carried along, with varying degrees of speed, the components of the plant pigment which was being analyzed. Those components which were more readily soluble in water tended to be retained on the filter paper, while the ones which were more soluble in the organic phase were carried along with the solvent. Thus, a series of concentric rings, corresponding to the various components of the pigments, formed on the filter paper. The position of these rings will depend on the kind of filter paper and the kind of solvent used. Since it is a constant quantity, it can be used as a means of identifying the components of a mixture.

I found that most of the anthoxanthins formed rings which were barely visible in ordinary light, but became visible under an ultraviolet lamp. Also, I found that practically all the flower pigments were mixtures of several components: usually one anthocyanin and several anthoxanthins. The xanthophylls, if present, were found on the solvent front, due to their insolubility in water and their ready solubility in alcohol.

I also attempted to develop the paper chromatograms with a 1% solution of sodium carbonate. I found that the sodium carbonate not only changed the color of the red and purple anthocyanins but also had a decided effect on the anthoxanthins. It made them very plainly visible in ordinary light, and intensified their fluorescence under ultraviolet radiation. In many cases, the color of fluorescence was affected by the sodium carbonate.

Effect of Acids and Bases

I found that the water-soluble pigments were affected by treatment with an acid or a base. I carried out these experiments by using three filter papers for each flower. I dipped one filter paper into the original pigment solution, another into the pigment with an acid and a third one into the original pigment, then exposed it to the fumes of ammonia.

In the presence of hydrochloric acid, the anthocyanins appeared bluish-red and the anthoxanthins appeared green.

After being exposed to the fumes of ammonia, the anthocyanins turned blue and the anthoxanthins turned a bright yellow.

Some of the filter papers, when exposed to ammonia, turned green. This indicated that anthocyanins and anthoxanthins were both present. The green was a result of the yellow from the anthoxanthins and the blue of the anthocyanins.

I repeated this experiment by using test tubes containing the water-soluble pigments. When hydrochloric acid was added, most of the anthocyanins of the different flowers brightened. The anthoxanthins turned green.

Conclusion

Thus I have attempted to prove that what may seem to be a plant or flower of one color in reality is a combination of many colors—perhaps unseen by the naked eye—but exposed to view by the valuable techniques of today's science.

Bibliography

A. Books

Barrett, F. C. and Brimley, R. C. *Practical Chromatography*. Reinhold Publishing Corporation, New York, N. Y.: 1953.

Cramer, F. *Paper Chromatography*. Second Revision. Macmillan, London, England: 1954.

Miller, Erston V. *The Chemistry of Plants*. Reinhold Publishing Corporation, New York, N. Y.: 1957.

Miller, Erston V. *Within the Living Plant*. The Blakiston Company, Inc., New York, N. Y.: 1953.

Strain, Harold H. *Chromatographic Adsorption Analysis*. Interscience Publishers, New York, N. Y.: 1942.

B. Periodicals

Baker, Carl G. "Chromatography and Paper Electrophoresis," reprinted from *The Science Teacher*. Vol. XXIII, 1956.

Bate, E. C. and Smith. "Paper Chromatography of Anthocyanins and Related Substances in Petals," *Nature*. Vol. 161, 1948, p. 835.

Gaze, Thomas B. and Wender, Simon H. "Paper Chromatography of Flavonoid Pigments," *Science*. Vol. 109, 1949, p. 287.

Lockhard, J. David. "Paper Chromatography," *The American Biology Teacher*. Vol. XX, No. 1, January, 1958, p. 18."

See also "A Solar-heated Greenhouse," Chapter 10, Physics, 2.

1

IN THE COURSE of developing a process for the production of magnesium, James C. Hartman of Fort Wayne, Indiana, became interested in the great possibilities of titanium. Learning that the high cost of producing titanium was due to the complicated decomposition process, he decided to investigate the possibilities of producing titanium by a cheaper method. His project, "Electrolytic Decomposition of Titanium Dioxide," was exhibited at the Ninth National Science Fair.

"Discussion

Several excellent books on the subject were procured from our public library and a great deal of valuable information from current magazines, especially from *Modern Metals*. Literature from the Dominum Magnesium Company in Canada proved a great help by explaining the process commonly used to produce titanium and by pointing out that titanium is one of the few metals that will combine directly with nitrogen from the air, thus making it necessary for the reaction to take place in an inert gas atmosphere. The report indicated, too, that the future of titanium production lay in the development of an electrolytic decomposition process. With this in mind, I began working on the development of a process that would involve electrolytic decomposition. Since titanium dioxide is the compound currently used for the extraction of titanium, the first big problem was to find a suitable solvent for titanium dioxide. This solvent would have to melt at fairly low temperatures and be able to dissolve large amounts of titanium dioxide. I first tried a nitrate, because of the low melting point of most nitrates. In order to keep a uniform heat and effect the decomposition of the nitrate, a porcelain heater cone was used. With this, several nitrates were melted (magnesium nitrate, aluminum nitrate, potassium nitrate and strontium nitrate) but they did not dissolve an appreciable amount of titanium dioxide and the nitrates began to decompose when heated for any length of time.

After several unsuccessful attempts with the nitrate baths, I decided to abandon the electrolytic method of decomposition and try decomposing the titanium dioxide by passing it into an alcohol vapor chamber and applying heat. This experiment was set up according to the diagram in Fig. 1 of the appendix. The reaction intended was $2CH_3OH + 3TiO_2 \rightarrow 2CO_2 + 4H_2O + 3Ti$ but this reaction required a higher temperature than was practical. Eager to exhaust the possibilities of this method, I repeated this experiment, this time using a pyrex tube and an acetylene torch for heat. Instead of the alcohol vapor, producer's gas, acetylene propane and carbon monoxide were used this time. The pyrex tube melted before any decomposition of titanium dioxide occurred. Satisfied that this type of decomposition did not hold promise, I resumed the original plan and the search for a suitable solvent.

Further reviewing and reading brought to light a mineral called sphene, a mixture of calcium oxide, titanium dioxide and silicon dioxide. This seemed to point up the possibility of using glass as a solvent, and the fact that glass melted at a fairly low temperature gave further encouragement along this line. Having ground small pieces of glass into a fine powder, I added an equal amount of titanium dioxide. This mixture was then heated in a crucible, and the titanium dioxide dissolved very readily even when additional portions of the compound were added.

Electrolytic Decomposition

The electrolytic method for the decomposition of titanium dioxide consists of dissolving titanium dioxide in a mineral called sphene. Sphene is a mixture of titanium dioxide plus calcium oxide plus silicon dioxide. This mineral was produced artificially by crushing scrap transparent glass, which is a mixture of calcium silicate and silicon dioxide, and adding titanium dioxide to this. The mineral formed when the glass melted and dissolved the titanium dioxide. More titanium dioxide was added when the sphene was melted, so that there was an abnormal amount of titanium dioxide in the sphene. The temperature maintained in the cell was approximately 1700-1800° C. The glass will melt at approximately 1650-1710° C. This heat was sufficient for the reaction to take place, but since titanium will not melt until 1810° C., it would be more profitable to maintain a temperature in an excess of 1810° C. The titanium metal could then be tapped off periodically in a liquid state. The nature of the electrolyte also permits the addition of more titanium dioxide at any time. The metal as found in the cell was in the form of very fine powder at the negative pole, which is the wall of the cell. The metal was attached to the electrolyte, which made it necessary to leach it out with hydrochloric acid. Titanium metal is highly resistant to dilute hydrochloric acid, but the sphene is slowly attacked by it.

I rented 5 6-volt storage batteries and hooked them in multiples to supply the necessary electricity. The 5 batteries supplied about 500 amps., but the resistance in the cell and the connections greatly reduced this amount. The third time the process was tried a 7-volt, 500-amp. plating generator was used. The decomposition can begin as soon as the electrolyte is molten. The electrical resistance provided by the electrolyte is great enough to keep the electrolyte molten for a while after the external heat is turned off. The external heat was supplied by a 1,000,000 B.T.U. burner at the Sturgis Light Metals Foundry.

The specific gravity of sphene is 3.4 to 3.6, while the specific gravity of titanium is 4.5. The difference between the two specific gravities is great enough to allow a definite separation between the titanium and the electrolyte. The titanium will go to the bottom of the cell unless the cell is violently agitated.

The cell consists of a nipple three inches in diameter and four inches long, with a pipe cap on each end. A hole in one end allows the graphite (+) electrode and an asbestos diaphragm to enter the cell. The diaphragm is needed because the oxygen is readily dissolved in the glass as well as the electrolyte. The negative pole of the cell is the metal part (eg., the two pipe caps and the nipple).

The first cell did not have a carbon lining in it and was severely attacked by the electrolyte and combined with the titanium to form ferrotitanates. The idea of using a carbon lining came from the one used to protect the cells in aluminum production. The lining is made by mixing lampblack with tar and coating the inside of the cell with it. The cell is then heated to about 700° C. to drive off the volatile material in the tar, leaving the carbon.

The efficiency of the cell is difficult to determine when worked on a small scale, but it does seem to be considerably less expensive to operate than the normal decomposition process. The high temperature required and the resistance of the electrolyte tend to lower the amperage greatly. The anode also is attacked by the electrolytic decomposition of titanium dioxide more than by aluminum oxide. For every atom of titanium liberated, two atoms of oxygen are liberated; while for every two atoms of aluminum liberated, three atoms of oxygen are liberated. However, the process shows possibilities of overcoming these smaller handicaps with the greater advantages. The process is continuous in that the cell metal collects on the bottom of the cell and can be tapped off periodically. The titanium dioxide also can be added periodically to keep the process in operation. Also, in contrast to the conventional decomposition method, a less noble metal like magnesium or sodium is not needed for the decomposition. The only cost in producing the electrolyte is in crushing the glass and the cost of the titanium dioxide itself (rulite ore is about 6 cents a pound). The titanium would not have to be converted to titanium tetrachloride, thus saving the cost of chlorination.

Bibliography

Barksdale, Jelks; *Titanium*. New York: Ronald Press Co. 1949.

Bray, John L.; *Nonferrous Production Metallurgy*. New York: John Wiley & Sons. 1947.

Conant, James Bryant and Blatt, Albert Harold; *Chemistry of Organic Compounds*. New York: Macmillan Co. 1952.

Everhart, John Laurence; *Titanium and Titanium Alloys*. New York: Reinhold Publishing Corp. 1954.

Graham, A. Kenneth; *Electroplating Engineering Handbook*. New York: Reinhold Publishing Corp. 1955.

Liddell, Donald M.; *Handbook of Nonferrous Metallurgy*. New York: McGraw-Hill Book Co. 1945.

Longe, Norbert Adolph; *Handbook of Chemistry*. Sandusky, Ohio: Handbook Publishers, Inc. 1956.

Longsdorf, Alexander S.; *Principles of Direct-Current Machines*. New York: McGraw-Hill Book Co. 1940.

Schwarzkopf, Paul; *Powder Metallurgy*. New York: Macmillan Co. 1947.

Timm, H. A.; "The Potential Merits of Titanium and Titanium Alloys Produced by the Oxide Reduction Process." Presented at the A.I.M.E. Regional Reactive Metals Conference in Buffalo, New York, 1956."

2

When he was awarded the unusual opportunity of working in the University of California Radiation Laboratory during the summer of 1957, Neil Nininger of Larkspur, California, worked on the problem of how to make tantalum carbide filaments that would not develop localized hot spots and burn out prematurely. The TaC filaments, which theoretically should burn at 3800° C. for short periods, were to be used in the radiation laboratory mass spectrographs. Neil's investigation was so successful and was considered so important that he was invited to make a report on his work to the personnel of the entire laboratory. He submitted a report of his work, which he called "The Production of High Temperature Tantalum Carbide Filaments," as part of his entry in the Science Talent Search the following fall. He was judged one of the winners and was awarded one of the top scholarships. Section III of his report outlines the experimental results of his work.

"TaC, Ta_2O and Ta all have different crystal types, and the junctions of the various phases are poor electrical connections. Consequently, hot spots develop at these junctions of high resistance, burning out the filament. Thus, the problem becomes how to produce filaments whose phase junctions[1] are increased in area. When this is done the total resistance across the junction is lowered.

The effect of temperature on reaction rates is such that when a filament is run at a low heat (800° C.), the reaction is slowed to such an extent that the formation of the various phases can be observed. Under this condition, Ta_2C first forms in the hottest part of the filament, the region noted as "A" in Figure 2. As the Ta_2C has a higher resistivity than the Ta metal, the "A" region becomes hotter and begins to extend itself over the length of the filament. At the same time, TaC forms in the hottest part of the "A" region, at "B." The TaC formed has a lower resistivity than the surrounding Ta_2C, and forms a cold spot. The cold region of TaC extends itself along the filament, toward the Ta-Ta_2C

---

1. There must always be junctions, because the extremities of the filament are cooled below the reaction temperature by end conduction of the support.

junction. In a short time, the TaC reaches the Ta-Ta$_2$C junction and a very localized transition zone is formed. The resulting transition zone (Figure 3) has a high resistivity because of the low cross-sectional area of contact, and the poor electrical contact between different crystal types. The filaments burn out at this point.

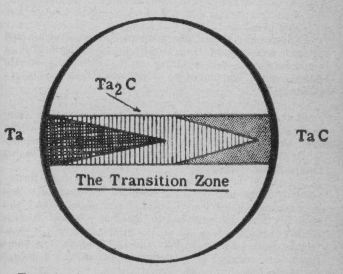

To make the area of contact gradual, I tried extending the transition zone over a larger length of the filament by carburizing rapidly. I flashed several filaments for short periods of time, at high temperature. This was to establish the Ta$_2$C crystal structure along the "table" of the filaments, and well down the "legs" (Figure 2). I then ran the filaments for long periods of time at low temperatures (800° C.), to form TaC over the Ta$_2$C crystal structure. But the transition zones were again too localized, and the filaments burned out. I tried the above procedure again, except that after flashing the filament I ran it for long periods of time at higher temperatures (1400° C.). However, the transition zones, although pushed down to the legs, became localized again, causing the filament to burn out.

After failing in this method of attack, I reinforced the legs of the filaments ("C" in Figure 2) with .004″ Ta foil strips. When the transition zones are pushed down to this reinforced region, they have a larger cross-sectional area with lower resistance. The reinforced transition zones also have higher mechanical strength. These factors enable filaments made by this last method to be used in mass spectrographs."

3

An interesting project that involved both construction and research was done by Leaf Turner, Brooklyn, New York, a member of the Honors Group of the Eighteenth Science Talent Search. The title of his project was "Hydrogen-Oxygen Fuel Cell."

"Recently, a device that has been known since the beginning of the century has finally received its deserved recognition. This is the fuel cell. The significance of the fuel cell is that electricity is generated directly from fuel by an electrochemical reaction.

Because of the importance that might result from further research concerning this cell, I decided last June to collect as much data about it as I could. Unfortunately, there was relatively little information. In the July *General Electric Review*, I came across an article on the fuel cell. I wrote to the authors, Dr. Liebhafsky and Dr. Douglas, requesting further information. They generously forwarded me enough for me to begin my work.

In July, also, in the *Journal of the Electrochemical Society*, I found "The Fuel Cell Round Table," which contained a summary of all the work that had been done on the fuel cell.

There were three kinds of fuel cells suitable for my project: a redox cell, a hydrogen-oxygen fuel cell, and a high temperature carbon monoxide-oxygen or hydrogen-oxygen cell. I decided that the hydrogen-oxygen cell was best suited for construction and laboratory experimentation.

Construction of Cell

The two porous graphite electrodes that I am using were obtained from two dry cells. I feared that the not too delicate strokes of the hammer necessary to break open the dry cells might cause the electrodes to break and that much time would therefore be lost. Fortunately, this was not the case.

At this point, my problem was to devise an efficient method of having oxygen adsorbed onto the surface of one electrode and hydrogen adsorbed onto the surface of the other. I cut off from the electrodes the ends having the metal binding posts. I obtained the use of a lathe with which I drilled a hole four inches into the electrodes from one of the ends. These holes had a diameter 1/8 inch greater than the diameter of the glass tubing, 3/16 inch, which I later inserted into these holes for the gas inlets. Half of my problem was solved, since the gas now would pass very close to the surface of the electrodes.

The other half of my problem was to obtain proper catalysts to adsorb these gases. With the help that General Electric offered me, I was able to choose my catalysts. For the hydrogen electrode I decided to use platinum from thermally decomposed platinic chloride; for the oxygen electrode I adopted the recommendation of Kordesch and Marko, which was a solution of 2.4 g $Co(NO_3)_2 \cdot 6H_2O$ plus 6.2 g. $Al(NO_3)_3 \cdot 9H_2O$ in 100 cc. of water.

In order to coat the surface of the hydrogen electrode, I poured a solution of platinic chloride into the center of the electrode. I heated the electrode until the water evaporated and the surface was coated with platinic chloride. Then I carefully heated the entire electrode until I saw a metallic coat on the electrode which I knew was thermally decomposed platinum.

In the other electrode, I evaporated 80 cc. of the nitrate solution and heated the entire electrode at 800° C. to convert the nitrates to oxides. I have had to take great care in the heating of these electrodes for fear that they might crack.

My next step was to find some type of cap to cover the openings of the holes, through which I could pass two tubes, one an inlet for the gas and the other an outlet. I decided to drill a three-quarter-inch hole into two one-holed rubber stoppers in order to cap the electrodes. This hole is smaller than the diameter of the electrodes, so that the stoppers might fit airtight over the electrodes. Then, through the side of the stoppers, I drilled a 3/16-inch hole to fit the outlets. After I put the stoppers over the electrodes and inserted into the holes the glass tubing for the inlets and outlets, I connected the inlets with an air supply. I found that a great amount of air was leaking from the area between the stoppers and the electrodes. In order to correct the leak, I used rubber cement. I found this unsatisfactory because the air, which was under considerable pressure, bubbled through the cement. Next I tried Duco cement. This seems to be serving my purpose well up to the present. I anticipate, however, that even the cement will not be completely satisfactory because it is inflammable. If necessary, I may try Miracle adhesive; but, here again, I may have the same problem.

At this point, I had to obtain a three-neck flask, in which I could put my electrolyte (KOH solution) and into which I could insert the two electrodes, and a Liebig condenser, which would condense any water that might evaporate from the electrolyte. I could not fit the electrodes into the necks of the flask I obtained, because the diameter of the necks was slightly too small. I decided to sand down the electrodes.

In the next phase of the experiment, I am going to fit the two electrodes into the two necks of the flask and a Liebig condenser into the third. My electrolyte will be a solution of 30% potassium hydroxide in water. Then I shall have to obtain my hydrogen supply.

Theory of Fuel Cell

The principle of this device is as follows. Oxygen molecules are adsorbed on the surface of the positive electrode. This adsorbed layer, being more active than molecular oxygen and being free, combines with the water in the electrolyte to form two hydroxyl ions. Each of these ions, having a single negative charge, removes an electron from the oxygen electrode, making the electrode positive. These hydroxyl ions migrate to the other electrode and combine with the adsorbed hydrogen to form water, depositing electrons in the process. Since the hydrogen electrode is negatively charged and the oxygen electrode is positively charged, electrons may flow through the external circuit. The following equations summarize the foregoing.

Hydrogen Electrode (Negative Pole):
$$H_2 = 2H$$
$$2H + 2OH^- = 2H_2O + 2e$$

Oxygen Electrode (Positive Pole):
$$\tfrac{1}{2} O_2 = O$$
$$O + H_2O + 2e = 2OH^-$$

Over-all Cell Reaction:
$H_2 + \frac{1}{2} O_2 = H_2O$

After I have my fuel cell working, I shall plot its various characteristics, e.g., current density versus voltage at different temperatures. Basing my information on what I have read on the low temperature hydrogen-oxygen fuel cell, I should obtain approximately .73 volts and a current density of 1 mA/cm^2.

Advantages of the Fuel Cell

As the world population increases, demand for electricity will increase. Fuel resources are constantly diminishing and the cost is rising. A more efficient and economical method of producing electricity must be devised.

The present method of producing electricity involves the use of steam engines. The efficiencies that have been obtained are about 30%. Thermodynamic laws set an upper limit on the efficiency.

The fuel cell, however, converts all chemical energy directly into electricity without the loss of energy incident to the use of steam engines.

Bibliography

1. *Journal of the Electrochemical Society* - Vol. 105, No. 7, July, 1958, pp. 428-431.
2. *General Electric Review* - July, 1958.
3. Fifth World Power Conference - *Recent Research in Great Britain on Fuel Cells*.
4. Bauer - OTS Report - *Fuel Cells.*"

4

An Honors Group Project of the Eighteenth Science Talent Search, entitled "Ozone and Sodium Hypochlorite," was done by Burton J. Krohn of Nashville, Tennessee.

"My project actually began with the building of a crude ozone generator as a chemistry project a year ago. The uniqueness of the chemical activity of this gas caused my interest in this subject to develop, and I decided to extend my work and research deeper, after further encouragement by an extra chemistry course last summer. The purpose of this project, as well as studying the effect of ozone on a hypochlorite bleach solution and quantitatively analyzing a solution of possibly four similar components, plus a gas, is to develop accurate and efficient scientific laboratory techniques.

The Ozone Generator

My ozone generator, simple but effective, consists of a 6-mm. pyrex glass tube bent into a right angle about 8 inches from one end and drawn into a jet about 10 inches in length at the other. The inner electrode is a 6-inch rat-tail file, and the outer electrode is aluminum foil wrapping. A 12,000-volt current produces a brush discharge around the glass. The flow of oxygen through the system is regulated by a homemade siphon mechanism and an adjustable pinch-cock, since an oxygen tank regulator costs over thirty dollars. The jet serves to enlarge contact surface area between gas and liquid as the oxygen-ozone mixture is bubbled through test solutions.

With moderate but growing success, I have kept the oxygen flow rate at 100 ml. per minute. Also to increase efficiency, water vapor, which catalyzes decomposition of ozone, is at least partially removed with calcium chloride. Despite precautions, the efficiency has constantly been hampered by leaks, which only recently I have succeeded in minimizing. The concentration of the ozone produced is approximately 1%.

Plan of Action

At the beginning of my project the question in my mind was whether ozone is sufficiently powerful to oxidize the chloride ion from the -1 oxidation state to $+1$ in hypochlorite, $+3$ in chlorite or $+5$ in chlorate. This question was answered by H. Willard and L. Merritt, Jr., in the 1942 Analytical Edition of *Industrial and Engineering Chemistry.* They said the change effected by ozone upon the chloride ion is negligible. I then turned to the possibility of raising hypochlorite from $+1$ to a higher oxidation state. I found no information about such a reaction; therefore I chose this question as a project.

In the reaction between ozone and a hypochlorite there is a possibility of five resultant products: unreacted ClO^-,

Cl^-, ClO_2^-, ClO_3^- and the gas ClO_2. The problem is the quantitative determination of each component and the establishment of proportions in which they occur. After considerable research into chemical properties of these compounds and possibilites (including ion exchange resins) for their separation and analysis, I decided upon the following steps (see equations):

Before Ozonation

1. Iodometric determination of total active oxygen content.
2. Argentometric determination of total chlorine content. ClO^- is reduced to Cl^- with hydrogen peroxide. This step accounts for any Cl^- formed by natural decomposition of ClO^-.

After Ozonation

1. Iodometric determination, in moles, of increase or decrease in total active-oxygen content. This test will not include ClO_3^-, if it is formed.
2. Argentometric determination of total chlorine content. ClO_2^- and ClO are reduced as in step 2 before ozonation. If total Cl is less than before ozonation, it may be due to one of two factors, or both. One possibility is the formation of ClO_3^-, which, as I proved by experiment, is not reduced appreciably by H_2O_2, even when the mixture is boiled. If ClO_3^- is formed, it can be quantitatively reduced to Cl^- by boiling with sodium nitrite. The other possibility is the loss of chlorine as ClO_2 gas, whose quantity can be calculated by subtracting the total Cl content after all reductions, from the total Cl content before ozonation.
3. Separation of ClO^- and ClO_2^-. The mixture is titrated against a slightly basic solution of arsenite, with which only ClO^- reacts, and quantitatively. Methyl orange solution is used as indicator.
4. Estimation of Cl^- formed during ozonation. If the total chlorine found in step 2 after ozonation is greater than the sum of the chlorine in all ClO^-, ClO_2^- and ClO_3^- determined after ozonation, then this difference resulted from one of two causes, or both. One possibility is the chloride ion formed during ozonation; the other is the remaining original chloride present before ozonation, due to previous decomposition of ClO^-. The chloride formed during ozonation may be calculated by subtracting this remaining chloride, which is the

difference in moles between steps 2 and 1 before ozonation, plus the combined number of moles of ClO^-, ClO_2^- and ClO_3, from the total chlorine found in step 3.

Results

As of now I am well into step 1 after ozonation, and I have also begun work on more difficult step 2. In each test in the first step 2000 cc. of O_2—O_3 mixture is bubbled through 30 ml. bleach solution diluted to 1/100 of its original strength. Fifty ml. of 0.02 M potassium iodide solution, plus 1 ml. of 99% acetic acid, is used in the titration flask, and a standard 0.005 M solution of sodium thiosulfate is titrated against the liberated iodine. My starch indicator suspension (as recommended in "Iodometric Determination of Inorganic Substances," *Volumetric Analysis, III*) was prepared by making a paste of 2 g. cornstarch plus 1 mg. mercuric iodide as a preservative in 30 ml. distilled water, and adding this to sufficient boiling water to make 1 liter. I found this preparation to be very satisfactory in providing precise, clear end-points.

Recorded are results of twenty-seven tests (see table), which vary so widely that their average cannot be considered conclusive. However, without exception, in each test the total active oxygen after ozonation is less than in the tests taken each day before ozonation, but the average number of moles lost is equal to only 3.2-4.7% of the amount of ozone used. Perhaps after tabulation of about sixty tests a more accurate figure may be obtained.

In my work in step 2, I add 2-3 ml. of full-strength hydrogen peroxide to 30 ml. test solutions, and boil for 5 minutes. The Cl^- formed is titrated against 0.01 M silver nitrate, using precipitation of red silver chromate as indicator. The major difficulty is distinguishing the end-point, which is not as clear as the starch indicator in iodometry. Ten inconsistent tests have shown my need for more practice in this titration.

Steps 3 and 4 remain in the future until my other data show conclusive results, and my familiarity with, and habits in, the chemical laboratory further improve.

I believe that this project in its planning, experimenting and calculating has thus far helped to develop, through failure and success, my persistence and attitude as a scientist.

Important Equations

1. Iodometric determination of active oxygen:
   a. Hypochlorite (iodide solution is acid):
   $$3HClO + KI \rightarrow KIO_3 + 3HCl$$
   $$KIO_3 + 5KI + 6HC_2H_3O_2 \rightarrow 3I_2 + 3H_2O + 6KC_2H_3O_2$$
   (One ClO^- is equivalent to one I_2)
   b. Chlorite:
   $$3HClO_2 + 2KI \rightarrow 2KIO_3 + 3HCl$$
   (One ClO_2^- is equivalent to $2I_2$)
   c. Iodine and thiosulfate - starch indicator:
   $$I_2 + 2Na_2S_2O_3 \rightarrow 2NaI + Na_2S_4O_6$$
   (One I_2 is equivalent to $2Na_2S_2O_3$)
2. Argentometric determination of chloride ion:
   $$NaCl + AgNO_3 \rightarrow NaNO_3 + AgCl$$
   Equation for indicator:
   $$Na_2CrO_4 + 2AgNO_3 \rightarrow 2NaNO_3 + Ag_2CrO_4 \text{ (red)}$$
3. Arsenite method for separating ClO^- and ClO_2^-:
   (methyl orange indicator):
   $$Na_2HAsO_3 + NaClO \rightarrow Na_2HAsO_4 + NaCl$$
   (Arsenic oxidized from $+3$ to $+5$)
4. Reduction of hypochlorite (or chlorite) with hydrogen peroxide:
   $$NaClO + H_2O_2 \rightarrow NaCl + H_2O + O_2$$
5. Reduction of chlorate with sodium nitrite:
   $$NaClO_3 + 3NaNO_2 \rightarrow NaCl + 3NaNO_3$$

Bibliography

1. Jacobson, C. A., *Encyclopedia of Chemical Reactions.*
   (a) "Arsenic," Volume I (1946), pp. 326-342.
   (b) "Chlorine," Volume II (1948), pp. 701-719, 725-731.
   (c) "Oxygen," Volume V (1953), pp. 295-300.
2. Samuelson, *Ion Exchangers in Analytical Chemistry,* Chapter II, "Fundamental Properties of Ion Exchangers," Chapter V, "Ion Exchange in Column Operation," Chapter VI, "Technique of Ion Exchange Separations for Analytical Purposes," 1956."

See also "The Behavior of Soap Bubbles and Films," Chapter 10, Physics, 3.

1

"EMAG III, a Checker-playing Digital Computer," was the name of the project presented by finalist David S. Ecklein, Cedar Falls, Iowa, at the Tenth National Science Fair.

"Introduction

My project, a digital computer programed to play a reasonable game of checkers with a human as its adversary, is the logical culmination of a previous active interest in electronics and symbolic logic. Its conception dates back to the summer of 1957 and since then has been the focal point of my efforts and aspirations. The project has in its entirety been developed in my home laboratory.

Indicative of the physical scope of this endeavor are the 3200 vacuum tubes, over 3000 sockets, 200 germanium diodes, thousands of resistors and miles of soldered wire circuitry which in part comprise its material aspect.

The design and construction demanded rigorous scheduling and utilization of time. Semi-mass-production methods were adopted to make practical and feasible what initially appeared to be a tremendously complex, if not impossible, task.

The procurement of components posed a very real challenge because of my limited resources. Careful choice of materials from war and industrial outlets coupled with some ingenuity of circuit design and construction parameters accomplished the necessary economies.

Past savings plus part-time and vacation earnings provided a budget. Employment during the past summer at the IBM Poughkeepsie Research Laboratory not only helped financially but provided valuable and encouraging experience through associations with outstanding computer scientists and engineers.

Theory

Checkers being a relatively complex game characterized by many variables, disillusionment can result from the wrong approach to its logical analysis. My analysis regards the main

72

game as consisting of thirty-two simple subgames wherein only one elect square of their fields can contain a piece to be moved. The merit of a move is a result of a Boolean function involving conditions in the elect square and in its adjacent squares as variables. Hence the checkerboard is considered to consist of thirty-two fields. Switching attention from subgame to subgame, the computer searches for a move. Several scans of the thirty-two subgames are made, the first being conditioned to effect a move from an elect square only under the most optimum conditions. If the first fails to produce a result, the next scan looks for a move of less merit. Thus the possible moves are ranked into categories as in the following list, inversely as to merit.

I.   Multiple jump using single man
II.   Multiple jump using king
III. Single jump involving no risk
IV.   Exchange using single man
V.   Exchange using king
VI.   Dangerous or undesirable jumps using single man
VII. Dangerous or undesirable jumps using king
VIII. Defend a man in danger, or escape being jumped
IX.   Traps, including two for one shots, breeches and forks
X.   Back men to build strong positions
XI.   Mediocre moves that do not immediately affect the position
XII. Moves using single man involving risk of trap
XIII. Moves using king involving risk of trap
XIV. Moves definitely losing single man
XV.   Moves definitely losing king

In addition to those previously listed, two transient categories are recognized and are shifted as to relative merit in accordance with the stage of the game and the possession of the move or opposition, to be explained later: T_1—force exchange, and T_2—challenge the enemy.

My analysis incorporates a number of general principles which in theory produce a consistent strategy of play. Authorities consider the game as divided into three consecutive stages: opening, midgame and endgame.[1] The first of these

1. Louis C. Ginsberg, "Principles of Strategy in the Game of Checkers" (New York, 1945), pp. 10-11.

includes the initial moves which must be made with consideration to avoid subsequent forfeit. Following this stage the second or body of the game is reached.[2] When play has progressed to the point where six or less pieces remain on the board for each adversary, it is recognized that the endgame has been reached.[3]

Inasmuch as the opening consists of eight or fewer moves,[4] I have combined it and the midgame into a single phase. The separate strategies of the opening-midgame and the endgame phases encompass two areas: first, the order of selection of subgames for consideration of the actual piece to be moved; and second, the relative importance of the transient categories."

The paper then analyzes the opening-midgame strategy, the strategy for the endgame phase and the importance of choosing the proper direction of motion. Because the computer lacks the faculty to memorize proper endgame forcing techniques, it is inadequate to cope with an average to good human opponent.

The next section describes how the computer was built.

"Components

Circuit components were chosen after rigorous experimentation. Suitability and availability made the 7193 surplus tube my choice for application throughout. Repeated trials indicated the choice of resistor values for the Eccles-Jordan trigger circuits and the inverter circuits. Zip-in type sockets were selected to expedite construction. Office shelving provided inexpensive and flexible chassis material. Perforated masonite served as paneling. Discarded pinball machines contributed some parts, including the field selector switch and stepping switches.

Input-Output Console

The input-output console comprises a display panel as well as the power supply and control panel. The display panel

2. *Ibid.*, p. 11.
3. *Ibid.*
4. *Ibid.*, p. 10.

incorporates two functions, the board display and the move display.

Ninety-six Eccles-Jordan trigger circuits, incorporating neon indicators arranged in checkerboard design, three in each of thirty-two squares, are the basis for the board display. The human player manipulates these indicators by means of a test-prod and screw-stud arrangement. The move display is an array of thirty-nine neon indicators and trigger circuits. This display indicates the square containing the piece to be moved for the machine, and also the direction and type of move to be made.

The power supply is of two parts, the B+ plate supply, and the C- bias supply. The plate supply operates directly from the power line and utilizes a half-wave bank of selenium rectifiers giving an output of 150 volts D.C. at 10 amperes. Filtering is accomplished by a bank of electrolytic capacitors totaling 1750 microfarads. Bias voltages of 25 volts at 5 amperes is derived from a transformer and full-wave rectifier arrangement with 10,000 microfarads of filtering. Tube heaters are connected in series-parallel to operate directly from the power line. This was attempted after experiments to establish the heater-cathode breakdown voltages of the tubes.

The control panel includes five fuse-box switches, which control the five blocks of heaters. Each block draws 5 to 15 amperes. Other fuse boxes handle the plate and bias voltage supplies. Meters keep vigil on the power supply voltages and amperages.

The Matrix Section

The matrices in this computer are of two types: triode and diode. The triode matrices comprise about 1500 tubes and are used in the field selection switching. They are nothing more than aggregates of inverters with common cathodes, plates and grids to economize on resistors. The diode matrices serve to build up off-board conditions for the field and to activate trigger-circuit aggregates.

The Logic Section

This is the decision-making organ. It contains the inverters, diodes and resistors necessary to simulate the category logic. It is the heart of the computer.

The Executive Section

This section encompasses the field scanning selector switch and motor, the category selector, the direction of move selector and other sequence of play apparatus.

Conclusion

This project is my most valued and significant scientific experiment. While EMAG III was developed as a mere game-playing device, the processes of solution and strategy involved are related to all machine decision making as applied to scientific or commercial problems. It has expanded my knowledge, developed my creative skills and definitely directed my interest into a field in which I hope to have a future career.

Acknowledgment

I wish to express appreciation for the encouragement received from my parents, teachers and friends. Most especially do I value the inspiration and guidance contributed by Dr. Arthur L. Samuel of the IBM Poughkeepsie Laboratory and by Dr. C. W. Farr of the Lincoln Laboratory at the Massachusetts Institute of Technology. I am grateful to the IBM Corporation for the experience provided me while employed at the Poughkeepsie Research Laboratory during my summer vacation.

Bibliography

Call, W.T. *Vocabulary of Checkers*. New York: Schlueter, 1909.

Doran, Peter. *Doran's Old 14th*. Chicago: Frank R. Wendemuth, 1936.

Duffy, J.M. *Duffy's Single Corner*. Chicago: Frank R. Wendemuth, 1934.

Elementary Checkers. Buffalo, New York: Wales Checker System, 1950.

Friel, Leonard G. *Checkers*. Chicago: Leonard G. Friel, 1940.

Ginsberg, Louis C. "Principles of Strategy in the Game of Checkers." New York: The *American Checkerist* magazine, 1945.

Hill, James. *Hill's Manual*. London: E. Marlborough, N.D.

Hopper, Millard. *How to Win at Checkers*. Buffalo, New York: Wales Checker System, 1956.

Lees, James. *Lees' Guide*. London: E. Marlborough, 1893.

McKay, Paul. *Easy Lessons in Checkers* reprint. Buffalo, New York: Wales Checker System, N.D.

Patterson, W. *How to Play Checkers*. Girard, Kansas: Haldeman-Julius, N.D.

Pickering, S.J. *Modern Magic* reprint. Buffalo, New York: Wales Checker System, N.D.

Sivetts, B. Frank. *Sivetts' Original and Infallible Method*. Oberlin, Ohio: Pearce and Randolph, 1894.

Spayth, Henry. *Checkers for Beginners*. Chicago: Stein, N.D."

2

"The Logical Mouse" was a project done by Roger Roberts, Baltimore, Maryland, finalist at the Ninth and Tenth National Science Fairs, and member of the Honors Group of the Eighteenth Science Talent Search.

"For many years the mouse has been the subject of conditioning experiments using shock and drugs. He has learned to remember sequences of problems, such as which path to traverse to reach his food. Since my project concerns the logical thought processes for working out a similar problem, I decided to use the mouse as a subject. However, my mouse is not a living organism, but merely an indicator of a transport mechanism. And to replace the mouse's brain I use a computer.

Background

The first high-speed computer, the Mark I, was introduced in 1944. It was developed as a means of performing complex mathematical computations rapidly. The first true electronic computer, ENIAC, was capable of speeds several thousand times as fast, and calculations which would have taken many man-months to perform were completed in minutes.

These first computers were digital, solving problems by simple binary counting. Many functions could be more efficiently handled by analog means, and complete or partial analog computers were designed.

The next stage of computer design was its application to the generating and maintaining of business records. This type of computer does not have to be a genius at solving problems. It must be able to perform many simple operations, store a large volume of data, change records rapidly and print out many different types of information.

There is no doubt, however, that the greatest value of the computer will be realized when its most recent application, that of logical reasoning, is fully developed. The Logical Mouse is a demonstration of this type of computer.

Design

For a system to be considered a computer it must have four basic elements: input, control, memory and output. Without these elements, it could not perform its basic functions of solving problems.

The problem that I undertook to solve was the tracing of an unknown maze by a mouse in the search for food.

The input element permits data to be read into the system. Input information can be delivered by punched tape, punched cards, special typewriters, magnetic tape, impulses or control positions.

The input of my Mouse is the impulses generated by a photoelectric eye seeing barriers which are set up to form the maze.

The control function establishes the program for the proper manipulation of the input data. It can be built into the computer, established by push buttons or patch cards, inserted as additional input or any combination of these.

My control stops the Mouse when it sees a barrier, turns it to find a clear path and signals the memory bank as to the correct direction.

The memory element provides a repository for information so that it can be obtained when needed. Memory can be internal or external. Forms of memory are punched tape, punched cards, magnetic tapes, magnetic drums, magnetic disks, magnetic cores, relays, vacuum tubes, sonic delay lines, electrical delay lines and cathode-ray tubes. The selection of the type of memory depends upon the amount of information to be stored, the desired speed of access, requirements for random access, the size of the computer and the economic factor.

Since I had a relatively small amount of information to

store, I decided to use a relay system. Relays offer direct control, efficiency, low cost, and can be reset by turning the power switch off and on.

The output, or the end product of a computer system, can take many forms. To name a few: punched tape, punched cards, magnetic tape, high-speed printing, cathode-ray display and control signals.

The output of my Mouse directs it through the maze, signaling the correct turn each time a barrier is reached.

Operation

The Mouse's movements are carried out by a transport mechanism beneath the maze. This mechanism moves a carriage horizontally and vertically. A magnet on the carriage is rotated by a motor. The Mouse is thus joined magnetically to the carriage and any motion of the magnet is repeated by the Mouse.

The photoelectric sensing unit consists of two parts, one in the Mouse and one in the carriage. The Mouse has two eyes, one of which contains a light source and the other the photoelectric cell. The light and cell are aimed so that when their paths converge on a barrier the Mouse will be positioned correctly before it rotates. There is a second light source on the underside of the Mouse which is directed at a photoelectric cell on the carriage. When the cell in the Mouse receives the reflected light from the barrier, it completes a circuit to the second light source. When this second light is energized, it signals the cell on the carriage and a relay is energized which causes the Mouse to stop moving.

Another relay is energized and the Mouse rotates 90° in a counterclockwise direction, searching for an unobstructed path. If there is no barrier, the Mouse will proceed until it is halted by another barrier farther on. But, if it senses a barrier in the same box after its first turn, the Mouse will rotate 180° in a clockwise direction by means of an energized relay before it starts moving horizontally or vertically along the maze after its rotation. This procedure continues until it reaches its destination (food), the lower left-hand box. Each time the Mouse encounters a barrier and only makes a left turn, the memory relay for that barrier retains that information by not being energized. But if the opening is on the right, the memory relay is energized and thus "remembers" that the correct path is to the right.

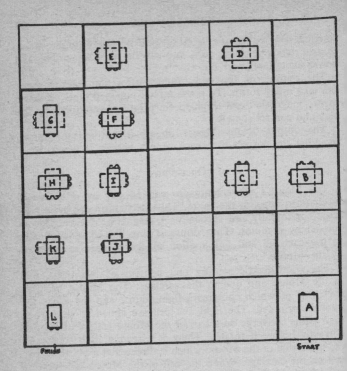

A TYPICAL PROBLEM

A—Mouse starts
B—Sees barrier, turns left
C—Sees barrier, turns left, sees barrier, turns right
D—Sees barrier, turns left
E—Sees barrier, turns left
F—Sees barrier, turns left, sees barrier, turns right
G—Sees barrier, turns left
H—Sees barrier, turns left
I—Sees barrier, turns left, sees barrier, turns right
J—Sees barrier, turns left, sees barrier, turns right
K—Sees barrier, turns left
L—Mouse reaches food

On second run Mouse will not make incorrect turns. When the correct path is to the left, it will turn left; when the correct path is to the right, it will turn right.

When the Mouse makes its second trip through the maze, it again stops as it sees each barrier. The memory is searched for the correct turn, and the Mouse will then move either right or left, depending upon the setting of the memory relay for that barrier. After the Mouse completes its turn it starts to move again, stops again at the next barrier, turns as the memory indicates and then moves on. It continues this procedure until it again reaches its destination.

Inspiration

The inspiration for my project came from reading an article describing a mechanical mouse that learned its way through a maze. Further investigation disclosed that it operated on the principle of stopping in each box and investigating all exit possibilities before proceeding. I felt it would be more meaningful to design one operating on principles that would simulate logical thinking, that is, not stopping until a barrier is encountered.

Conclusion

I call this the "Logical Mouse" because its actions are made in a logical manner. It follows a pattern of "looking" first left and then right, and remembers only the correct information. Computers, working on similar reasoning principles, can, by examining all pertinent information, predict weather or elections, navigate ships or missiles, control factory production, direct traffic patterns and perform many other tasks.

The potential of this type of computer is limited only by human imagination. For example, an apartment house could be designed for maximum efficiency, or an entire city could be planned. A master control could handle all municipal services automatically. A new product could be completely engineered, and then built directly by output signals controlling automatic production equipment. I hope someday to design one of these computers."

See also "Some Investigations into the Relationship between Symbolic Logic and Electronic Switching Networks," Chapter 8, Mathematics, 2.

1

THIS is an excerpt from the project "The Effects of Temperature on the Toxicity of Insecticides," presented by finalist Bill Boyer of Fayetteville, Arkansas, at the Ninth National Science Fair.

"In the investigation for this project I exposed insects to definite dosages of insecticides for twelve hours to determine if varied temperatures would effect the toxicity of the insecticides used.

The method I used was relatively simple. I took very concentrated insecticides and diluted them in two or three steps. In the first two of these steps I diluted them with water. In the last step I diluted with a solution of 1 part Karo and 2 parts water. (I used ordinary Karo syrup from the store.) The Karo was put in the solution as food for the flies. I added 1 ml. of the insecticide, Karo and water solution to a 60-ml. glass vial containing 1.5 gm. of powdered clay. The powdered clay was to give the mixture consistency or texture. I used dilutions of insecticide at such rates as ½ part of insecticide to a million parts of Karo-water solution, 2 parts per million, and 40 parts per million. I had to test many different rates to find the right one to give a good pattern of kill. For instance, too much insecticide would kill all of the insects and too little would not kill any.

I stirred the clay and the insecticide solution with a glass stirring rod until it made a paste. Then I spread the paste on the wall of the vial, about halfway up. I applied the paste to the wall to give it more surface area.

I then used an aspirator, which is a common device for sucking insects into vials, and put ten fruit flies into each vial. I used fruit flies, for they are (1) standard testing animals, (2) easy to rear in great numbers, (3) easy to handle and (4) easily obtainable.

I took the vials with the flies in them, corked them up and put them in a controlled temperature for twelve hours. The temperature chambers were thermostatically controlled. At the end of twelve hours I counted the number of dead flies and

Aspirator, device for putting insects into vials, and illustration of insecticide, clay and Karo-water solution in vial

KEY

1. 60 ml. glass vial

2. Cotton to keep insects from escaping

3. Fruit flies

4. Aspirator—consists of two-hole rubber stopper, glass tubing, rubber tubing

5. Mouthpiece for "sucking" up insects

6. 60 ml. glass vial used in temperature chambers

7. Insecticide, clay and Karo-water solution on side of vial

8. Cheesecloth for keeping insects out of mouth

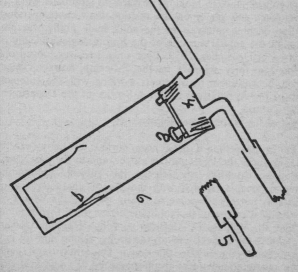

recorded the results. Death was defined as occurring when all visible motion had ceased or when they were unable to right themselves after being placed on their backs. I used chambers with temperatures of 50°, 60°, 70° and 80°F. I had a 90° box available but my controlled check indicated that a 90° heat without insecticide killed 95% of the insects. Therefore it was not used in the other experiments.

I ran tests on four insecticides. In each test I had four vials for each temperature. I replicated each test four times. The results have been based upon the study of 160 insects. The graphs that are included illustrate the exact figures of the kill. But the general trend shows that the higher the temperature, the more the kill, with the exception of DDT, which works the opposite—the higher the temperature, the less the kill."

2

"A Study of the Firefly and the Chemical Nature of Its Bioluminescence" was started by Leland N. Edmunds, Jr., of North Miama, Florida, a year or so before he entered the Fifteenth Science Talent Search. Lee has recently graduated from college and is looking forward to graduate work in entomology. His paper on the relation between temperature and the flashing intervals of the adult male firefly was presented at the annual meeting of the Entomological Society of America in December, 1959. Ever since Lee was judged one of the top forty winners in the Fifteenth Science Talent Search, he has spent his summers working with the entomologists of the Agricultural Research Service of the Department of Agriculture.

Part of his Search paper follows.

"For a long time I have been curious to know exactly what produces the lightning bug's light, and in the past year I have done extensive research on this subject. By reading widely, I became familiar with the general characteristics of the firefly, but I was unable to obtain any specific details on the chemical nature of its bioluminescence. With this in mind, I wrote Dr. William D. McElroy of Johns Hopkins University, who is experimenting with the firefly, asking him for any information pertaining to this topic. He sent several pamphlets and some adenosine triphosphate (ATP) and said that it would be very convenient if someone could discover a method for growing these organisms in the laboratory. He also suggested, as a project, the collection of eggs from females onto various media to determine whether it is possible to raise these eggs into larval forms.

I decided to divide my project into two sections: (1) attempts to raise fireflies and related experiments; and (2) study of the biochemistry of the firefly's luminescence. I will present my report under these two headings.

Attempts to Raise Fireflies and Related Experiments

My first step was to obtain the fireflies, and I immediately encountered an obstacle—there was a scarcity of fireflies in my region this year. Their season is supposed to last from June through August, but the first one I saw appeared in late August and the last one on October 6!

I usually hunted the insects with a net in a large field near my house from about 6:30 to 7:30 p. m., and I was fairly successful. Enclosed is a chart indicating the number of fireflies I caught each night, along with other details.

While catching fireflies I was able to observe many other things firsthand, some of which verified what I had read previously. I discovered that as the evening progresses, the fireflies rise to high altitudes, a phenomenon which, to the best of my knowledge, has not been explained.

I also learned much about the firefly's romantic habits, for the flash of light is a signal between the sexes. The female climbs to the top of a blade of grass or a shrub and flashes her light to attract a male. The males fly slowly along near the ground, looking for the females and flashing on the average of once every 5.8 seconds. The female signals back every 2.1 seconds, and thus the male is guided toward her and finally mates with her. I determined these intervals of response with a stop watch. To do this, it was necessary to take numerous readings and find an average, for the interval is directly proportional to the temperature, decreasing on hot evenings and increasing if the night is chillier. I tried to find this exact relation, but I was unable to make enough readings to determine anything conclusive.

I had read that it was possible to decoy the males by placing a flashlight in the grass and signaling with the correct interval of response. I tried this but only was able to make the males hesitate in their flight. However, I had greater success in decoying the females. I took a flashlight, covered it partially with my hand and flashed it suddenly in the characteristic check-mark pattern of the male, about every 5.5 seconds. After three trials, a female answered me from about four yards away, and I tracked her down.

Measuring the time intervals also helped me to identify the species common to my locality as *Photinus pyralis*, which is the only common eastern firefly with these intervals of response, since nature has developed a specific rhythm for each species.

Also, I determined that the average life span of my fireflies, all of which were subjected to the same abnormal conditions, was 5.4 days.

The fireflies I caught I placed in various modified terrariums, hoping that they would mate and lay eggs.

On September 17, I managed to secure a pair and put them in a separate container. They copulated for forty-five minutes, but no eggs were produced, and the female died soon after. Other attempts to get males and females to mate failed. Then, on September 24, I discovered a pair beginning to copulate in the field. I carefully removed them to a jar, and they mated for one and a half hours. . . .

On September 27 I discovered nine yellowish-white true spherical eggs on the leaves of the plant in the terrarium and on the container's sides. Nine more eggs were laid on September 29, making a total of eighteen. I made a slide of two, and the rest I placed on a plant in another terrarium and on a piece of moist wood. These were kept at about 65°F. Some of the eggs shriveled up, but by December 10 I still had five of them left, and still unhatched. Then, a rat knocked over the terrarium, and my hopes were destroyed. However, I am planning to try again next year to raise fireflies.

Meanwhile, the last of my other fireflies had died on October 14, bringing to a close this part of my project.

Study of the Biochemistry of the Firefly's Luminescence

I have just started working on this part of my project, as most of my time has been spent collecting the fireflies for it as outlined in the preceding part. Briefly, the firefly's light is produced by the oxidation of a substance called luciferin in the presence of a catalyst, luciferase. However, only one flash could be obtained unless there was present adenosine triphosphate (ATP), a high-energy phosphate compound which reduces the oxyluciferin to luciferin again after each flash. These reactions can be described by the following equation: Luciferin $+$ Luciferase $+$ Mg $+$ ATP $+$ O$_2$ $\rightarrow$ Light $+$ Oxyluciferin $+$ Etc.

I dissected the tails from the fireflies I caught, ground several of them up and added a solution of ATP in an effort to produce light. However, this was unsuccessful, even when I added Mg. In the latter experiment, the tails changed from bright yellow in color to a dull brownish-yellow. I can think of at least two reasons for my failure: (1) The tails have become inactive; (2) I did not use enough lanterns. The latter is almost insurmountable, for I cannot use any more as I have only 17 mg. of firefly lanterns altogether.

If I can somehow obtain some more fireflies, I plan to extract and purify the luciferase and luciferin in their tails. However, in the procedure outlined by Dr. McElroy (see Diagrams #1 and #2) 5 gm. of lanterns are required. I also hope to test for the presence of ATP in various tissues with ground-up firefly lanterns. Another spectacular experiment is to make one solution of luciferin and one of luciferase (luciferase is unstable in hot water and thus luciferin could easily be obtained) and pour them together, thus producing liquid light.

Hence, future progress depends on my securing more firefly tails. I have just written to Dr. McElroy on this matter, asking his advice and inquiring whether preserved fireflies from biological supply houses would serve the purpose. In any event, however, I plan to continue my work on the firefly throughout the coming year."

1

SONIA Ruth Anderson of Omaha, Nebraska, a winner in the Sixteenth Science Talent Search, wrote a report on seven years of "fooling around" with her fossil collection. It was called "The Collection, Study and Classification of Some Eastern Nebraska Fossils."

"In the autumn of 1950, I began to collect, study and classify numerous eastern Nebraska fossils. My objective was to determine some of the organisms which existed here during prehistoric times and to learn something about them. I've gathered my entire collection, except for the Pliocene specimens, by myself.

Field Observations (See Map, Plate 42)

Most of my field work has been confined to the Pennsylvanian shales and limestones and to the Dakota Cretaceous sandstones in the eastern sections of both Cass and Sarpy counties.

Fossils in Cass and Sarpy Counties

Thin carbonaceous Pennsylvanian shale strata seem to contain comparatively few fossils. While cleaving these shales I've found Calamites (Plate 40) and the impression of a ganoid (Frontispiece), which is quite rare.

I recognized the thick Pennsylvanian limestone strata by the presence of the index fossil *Fusulina secalica* (Plate I). These limestone exposures are often weathered, so that many nearly perfect fossil coelenterates, bryozoans, brachiopods, echinoderms and, occasionally, mollusks, trilobites and sharks teeth may be collected from the residual debris.

Pennsylvanian strata seem to indicate the termination of the Paleozoic rocks in this locality, because the Permian deposit seem to be absent.

Between the Pennsylvanian and the overlying Dakota Cretaceous formations, I observed the absence of Triassic and

88

Plate 1

CLASS SARCODINA

ORDER FORAMINIFERA

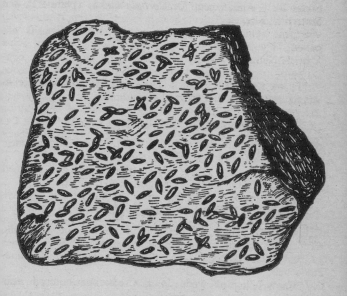

Fusulina secalica
natural size

**Locality: Plattsmouth, Nebraska
Period: Pennsylvanian**

Jurassic strata. During the Triassic and Jurassic periods, most of Nebraska was elevated, so that weathering and erosion obliterated all representative fossils and rock deposits except deep in the western portion of Nebraska.[1]

Dakota Cretaceous ferruginous sandstones and conglomerates appear along the Missouri River bluffs near Plattsmouth and also near Louisville. These deposits seem to be nearly barren of fossils, except for *Corbula hicksii* (plate 22) and other mollusks.

Eocene, Oligocene, Miocene and Pliocene deposits are missing in this area.

A thin stratum of exposed Pleistocene glacial drift, consisting of granite and quartzite, overlies the Dakota Cretaceous formation near Cedar Creek. I've found no fossils either in this or in the loess and alluvial formations.

Transported Fossils in Sarpy County

Permian cephalopods (Plates 26-27) were found in chert railroad ballast, probably from Lancaster county.

Fossil bison teeth (Plate 37), petrified bones and petrified wood occur in the Platte River gravel at La Platte.

Fossils in Other Counties

I made a limited examination of an outcrop from the Cretaceous Greenhorn formation, consisting of large masses of *Inoceramus labiatus* (Plate 23), in a buff, chalky limestone near Ponca.

I found silicified wood in a Cretaceous outcrop near Niobrara.

The extensive Pleistocene glacial drift in Knox and Cedar counties has yielded no fossils.

My Procedure for Cleaning the Fossils

Many of my specimens were covered with limestone. The vise in which I placed each fossiliferous rock freed the fossils from their matrix. Immersion in hydrochloric acid or in vinegar removed any particles of limestone that I could not remove with a file.

---

1. Nebraska Geological Survey, 1903, vol. 1, p. 118.

Conclusions

Tropical, marine foraminiferans, corals, bryozoans, large numbers of brachiopods, sea urchins, crinoids and a few mollusks, trilobites, sharks and ganoids seem to have populated Cass and Sarpy counties during the Pennsylvanian period. A relative of the horsetails, Calamites, indicates that there probably was some elevated but swampy land.

Permian cephalopods and corals indicate that there probably was some sea in Lancaster county during the Permian period.

Many changes probably occurred in eastern Nebraska between the Pennsylvanian and the Cretaceous periods. Pelecypods, which represent the only phylum from the Pennsylvanian period which I've also found represented in the Cretaceous system, seem to have occupied a more important position in the Cretaceous period than they did during the Pennsylvanian period. Silicified wood in the Cretaceous system indicates that there probably was some elevated land with forests.

Ungulates seem to have been important during the Pliocene epoch. Oreodons, gigantic turtles, camels, prongbuck-like animals and rhinoceroses existed near Ainsworth.

Bison were in existence in the Pleistocene epoch, during which glaciation was taking place in Nebraska."

2

James Maxwell Bardeen of Champaign, Illinois, combined his two prime interests—geology and solid-state physics—in a project on thermoluminescence that helped him to become one of the forty winners of the Fifteenth Science Talent Search. He was able to use some of the specimens from his own rock collection in the experiments that led to his report on "The Thermoluminescence of Rocks and Minerals."

"Thermoluminescence has long been known to scientists, but it was only recently that a theory was developed by physicists to explain this phenomenon. When radiation of sufficiently high energy strikes a crystal, some of the electrons are freed from the valence bonds. Some of these freed electrons may become trapped by impurities or crystal defects at an energy level intermediate between that of valence electrons and that of free electrons. If these traps have a low energy level, the electrons cannot be freed unless considerable energy is imparted to them by something such as heat. Then the electrons may go to luminescent centers, where their excess energy is released as light. The trapped electrons are released at different temperatures, depending on the energy level of the trap. Thus the light is emitted in bursts as the crystal is heated up.

Much work has been done on the thermoluminescence of rocks and minerals by a research group at the University of Wisconsin under the direction of Farrington Daniels. Their final report, *The Thermoluminescence of Crystals*, is my main source of information on the subject. They conducted a general survey of the thermoluminescence of rocks and minerals and found limestone and granite to exhibit natural thermoluminescence in almost all cases. Artificial thermoluminescence occurs when the traps are filled by irradiation in the laboratory. Extremely small amounts of radioactivity acting over millions of years produce natural thermoluminescence. Glow curves, showing the amount of light corresponding to a given temperature as the specimen is heated at a uniform rate, were obtained for hundreds of samples by the Daniels group. No natural thermoluminescence was observed at temperatures much below 150° C., since ground heat acting over long periods of time evacuates the traps whose electrons require relatively little energy to be freed. The uses of thermoluminescence in correlating rock strata, in determining relative ages of limestones and in finding the ages of intrusions were among the special topics which received a good deal of attention.

Apparatus

. . . . A cone-shaped 600-watt electric heating element in a flowerpot serves as a "furnace" for heating my samples. The flowerpot rests on the porcelain socket with the cone coming up through an enlarged hole in the bottom of the flowerpot. Granular insulation was put around the cone to screen out glow from the heater and hold in the heat. The samples are placed on a metal plate which rests on top of the cone. . . .

An IP-28 photomultiplier tube is being used to obtain curves of light emission (glow curves). The voltage required comes from old 90-volt "B" batteries. . . . In order to increase the sensitivity of the apparatus, a condensing lens with a short focal length is placed between the specimen and the photomultiplier tube. . . .

Results and Future Plans

Since I am just getting started in the actual recording of glow curves, the quantity of my results is not very great as yet. Through the cooperation of Herbert D. Glass of the Illinois State Geological Survey I have received some fifteen specimens of limestone, most of which come from Illinois. In geological age they range from Pre-Cambrian to Pennsylvanian. With these specimens I hope to be able to establish some relation between glow curve shapes and ages. It seems most likely that this will be in connection with the heights of the lower temperature peaks of the glow curve. . . .

Interesting anomalies have arisen with two specimens which have been tested for thermoluminescence. Both specimens are from my collection. Calcite in a matrix of Galena limestone, which I found near Mineral Point, Wisconsin, was observed to thermoluminesce quite brightly. Generally the light came only from regions adjacent to the matrix. The matrix itself, a yellowish, crumbly limestone, didn't thermoluminesce noticeably. Perhaps the matrix has the radioactivity and the calcite the crystal structure required for thermoluminescence. A glow curve run on a piece of this calcite shows peaks at 190°, 250° and 340° C.

A specimen of La Salle limestone collected near Fairbury, Illinois, thermoluminesces quite brightly also. A fossil brachiopod from this limestone, however, exhibited no thermoluminescence; and the thermoluminescence that had been observed was spotty.

Along with investigating these phenomena I am planning to check on the thermoluminescence of different kinds of fluorite—particularly to see if there is a relationship between color and glow curve peaks. . . ."

1

NUMBER THEORY, statistical biology and game theory are some of the branches of mathematics that Science Talent Search winner John N. Mather of Princeton, New Jersey, enjoys exploring. His project report, "Nine Postulates for Euclidean Geometry," was part of his winning entry in the Nineteenth Science Talent Search.

John's very thorough paper has been abstracted here.

"Introduction

The purpose of this paper is to develop a set of postulates for Euclidean geometry, and to show two things about these postulates: that they actually are true of what we normally call Euclidean space, and that they describe only Euclidean space.

In accordance with these aims, parts of this paper are written in two different ways. When theorems are proved from the postulates, the vocabulary is limited to terms previously defined and a basic English vocabulary to connect these terms in sentences. When it is shown that the postulates actually are true of what is normally called Euclidean space, the vocabulary is not limited in this manner.

In this system of postulates, primitive terms are point and an undefined relation, written ab∠cd for points a,b,c,d. Although the relation ab∠cd is not defined, it may be interpreted as equivalent to the statement "b is less distant from a than d is from c." Such an interpretation is consistent with the given postulates.

Properties of the Undefined Relation

The first three postulates are as follows:
(In general, a vertical through the symbol for a relation will mean that the relation does not hold.)

Postulate 1. If a,b,c are points then ab∢cc.

94

Postulate 2. If $ab < cd$ then $cd \not< ab$, for any four points a,b,c,d.

Postulate 3. If $ab < cd$ and $ef \not< cd$ then $ab < ef$, for any six points a,b,c,d,e,f.

Two additional relations are now defined:

Definition 1. $ab > cd$ if and only if $cd < ab$.

Definition 2. $ab \simeq cd$ if and only if $ab \not< cd$ and $cd \not< ab$.

By application of the definitions, the statements in the following lemma follow immediately from the postulates.

Lemma 1.

a) For any points a,b,$ab \simeq ab$.

b) If $ab \simeq cd$ then $cd \simeq ab$, for points a,b,c,d.

c) If $ab < cd$ and either $cd < ef$ or $cd \simeq ef$ then $ab < ef$, for points a,b,c,d,e,f.

d) If either $ab > cd$ or $ab \simeq cd$ and $cd > ef$ then $ab > ef$, for points a,b,c,d,e,f.

The following lemmas require indirect proofs:

Lemma 2. If $ab \simeq cd$ and $cd \simeq ef$ then $ab \simeq ef$ for points a,b,c,d,e,f.

Proof. By definition 2, one of $ab < ef$, $ab \simeq ef$ or $ab > ef$ must hold. But by lemmas 1c and 1d, both $ab < ef$ and $ab > ef$ combine with one of the equalities in the hypothesis to give an inequality which contradicts the other equality in the hypothesis. Therefore $ab \simeq ef$.

Lemma 3.

a) If $ab \simeq cd$ and $cd < ef$ then $ab < ef$ for points a,b,c,d,e,f.

b) If $ab > cd$ and $cd \simeq ef$ then $ab > ef$ for points a,b,c,d,e,f.

Lemma 3a differs from the statement if $ab < cd$ and $cd \simeq ef$ then $ab < ef$, which is part of lemma 1c, because in lemma 3a (using the interpretation mentioned above) cd represents a *smaller* distance than ef and the same distance as ab, while in the other statement cd represents a *greater* distance than ab and the same distance as ef. Lemma 3b differs from the statement if $ab = cd$ and $cd > ef$ then $ab > ef$ in a similar way.

Proof of lemma 3a. By definition 2, one of $ab < ef$, $ab \simeq ef$, or $ab > ef$ must hold. If $ab \simeq ef$, it follows from the hypothesis $ab \simeq cd$ that $cd \simeq ef$ (by lemmas 1a and 2), contradicting the hypothesis $cd < ef$. The hypothesis $cd \simeq ab$ and the assumption $ab > ef$ give (by lemma 1d) $cd > ef$, a contradiction. Hence $ab < ef$.

Lemma 3b follows immediately.

After the following postulate, distance may be defined.

Postulate 4. If a,b are points then $ab \simeq ba$.

Definition 3. The *distance D(a,b) between the points a*

and b is the set of all the pairs of points c,d such that ab~cd.

This definition assigns a concrete object to that which is usually considered to be abstract, but it serves its purpose of guaranteeing that distance has all of its usual properties. In particular:

Theorem 1. $D(a,b)=D(c,d)$ if and only if ab~cd.

This follows from lemmas 1a, 1b and 2.

(Note: The convention shall be adhered to throughout that if a and b are two objects then a=b means that they are identical.)

Postulates of Denseness and Continuity

According to Dedekind's definitions, two properties that a line has are: a) denseness (between every two points is another point); and b) continuity (every cut of a line into two sets A and B, such that every point in A is to the left of every point in B, determines a point p such that: 1) every point in A is either p or to the left of p; and 2) every point in B is either p or to the right of p.) Among the properties that cannot be shown without postulates 5 and 6 are denseness and continuity.

Before postulates 5 and 6 can be stated, several definitions are desirable.

Definition 4.   The *spheroid S(a,b) with center* (or *of*) *a through b* is the set of all points p such that $ap<ab$.

Note that if a=b then S(a,b) is void.

Definition 5.   A point p is said to be a boundary point of set A if and only if every non-void spheroid of p contains points in A and points not in A.

Definition 6.   The *boundary F(A) of A* is the set of all boundary points of A. The *closure A* of A* is the union $A \cup F(A)$. Set A is *closed* if and only if $A \supset F(A)$; *open* if and only if $\bar{A} \supset F(A)$.

Note: The symbolism of set theory will be used. If A and B are sets, then the set of all elements

in A or in B	is the union $A \cup B$
in A and in B	is the intersection $A \cap B$
not in A	is the complement $\bar{A}$ of A

Both $A \subset B$ and $B \supset A$ mean A is a proper subset of B; $A \subseteq B$ and $B \supseteq A$ mean A is a subset of B; A=B means sets A and B are identical; a∈A means a is an element of set A. The symbol ϕ represents the void set (the set that has no elements).

Postulate 5.   If a,b are distinct points then c∈F(S(a,b)) if and only if ab=ac.

The following property of geometry, which is one that is true only for dense sets, follows from the previous postulates, lemmas and postulate 5.

Theorem 2. If a,b are distinct points then (a) there is a point $p \neq a$ in S(a,b) and (b) if for point c, $ac < ab$ then there is a point $p \epsilon S(a,b) \cap \overline{S(a,c)}$ *.

Proof. By postulates 1 and 5, $a \epsilon S(a,b)$ *. By definitions 5 and 6, $a \notin F(S(a,b))$, hence $a \epsilon S(a,b)$. But since a and S(a,c)* are closed, while S(a,b) is not, a and S(a,c)*, being subsets of S(a,b), must be proper subsets of S(a,b). But this is just another way of stating the conclusions of the theorem.

The continuity postulate is:

Postulate 6. If Q is any aggregate of closed subsets of some spheroid, such that sets $A, B \subset Q$ imply that one of $A \subseteq B$ or $B \supseteq A$ holds, then there is a point p contained in every set that is an element of Q.

The following two statements can be proved using postulate 6 alone.

(1) If A is any set and point $a \notin A$ *, then there is a point $p \epsilon F(A)$ such that $A^* \cap S(a,p) = \phi$.

Consider any point $j \epsilon A$. Then the aggregate Q of all sets $A^* \cap S(a,k)$ *, for $k \epsilon S(a,j)$ *, satisfies the given conditions in postulate 6, hence there is a point p in every such $A^* \cap S(a,k)$ *. This point p may be shown to satisfy the conclusion of the statement (1).

(2) If A is any subset of a spheroid then for any point a there is a point $p \epsilon F(A)$ such that $S(a,p) \supset A$.

This statement may be proven in a similar manner. . . .

The Postulate of Similarity

As of yet, the postulates given fail to distinguish between the form of space in which there are in any plane two lines through any given point parallel to each line in that plane (Lobachevskian space) and the form in which there is only one, Euclidean space. A property by which these two types of space may be distinguished is a rule of similarity of figures, which is in non-mathematical terms: any figure may have its position or size altered in any way without changing its shape.

Any two such figures are called similar. . . .

Conclusion

It has not yet been shown that the postulates given hold for only Euclidean geometry. To do this a set of coordinates could be set up to show that the rules of analytic geometry hold, analytic geometry being chosen because it is the most widely known form of geometry and therefore the most acceptable for showing what the postulates in this article describe. Such a process would be lengthy, involving developing theorems about angles and particularly about perpendiculars. It would also necessitate proving that through any point outside of a given line L there is one and only one line parallel to L and in the same plane as it is in. The author is certain, however, that this process can be carried out. . . ."

2

A graphic description of how a project can grow and expand into future work is abstracted here from the paper on "Some Investigations into the Relationship between Symbolic Logic and Electronic Switching Networks," which helped Edward Ganz of Bethesda, Maryland, to become one of the top forty winners of the Eighteenth Science Talent Search.

"Introduction

For many years, I have been interested in the field of mathematics. During the course of my reading, I encountered references to symbolic logic which immediately aroused my curiosity. This relatively new field seemed to offer numerous opportunities for individual research and investigations. Then I came across Claude Shannon's monumental work on the relationship of symbolic logic to electrical switching circuitry. As I had long been interested in electronics, the union of these two fields was particularly attractive to me.

In addition to my explorations into the purely mathematical aspects of symbolic logic, I directed my study to its use in the synthesis and analysis of switching networks and, conversely, the application of switching networks to pure logic. . . .

Progress has been made in showing that symbolic logic is a powerful tool for the analysis and synthesis of electronic switching systems. Little has been done, however, with the converse, namely, the application of electronic systems to the field of symbolic logic. During the course of my research, I became particularly interested in this second relationship. I decided to design and construct an electronic device which would provide extremely rapid solutions to complex problems in symbolic logic. To my knowledge, only two "logic machines" have been built: one at Manchester, England, and the other at M.I.T. I was able to learn little of these machines other than the fact that both were electromechanical. As a result, I proceeded on my own.

My prime interest was in the area of system development of the device as a logical unit. In other words, I was not at this time directly concerned with the design of, for example, a more efficient flip-flop circuit. As a result, by changing the values of the circuit parameters to meet my specific needs, I was able to utilize several tried and proven circuit configurations for my new applications. Several subassemblies presented rather unique requirements, however, and I decided to design these myself.

After much thought and experimentation, I arrived at the device described in the following pages. I have called it an electronic logical truth analyzer. Flexible, almost entirely automatic and unique in many respects, this device will provide the solution to literally millions of functions of up to 5 logical variables in a maximum of 32 milleseconds.

Logic Circuitry

The logical analyses performed by the machine are carried out by the process of electronic analogy. In effect, that part of the device termed logic circuitry is an electronic switching network whose operation is defined by the logical expressions under consideration. Each fundamental element of this network is the electronic representation of the mathematical expression which describes its function.

I decided upon the four logical constants "not," "and," "or" and "if . . . then . . ." as the elemental building blocks of the logic circuitry. They are both logically and electronically universal. Logically, these units may be used to build up complex system of thought containing practically all commonly used functions. Electronically, I have taken care of loading to the point where each block will drive any other, and a great number of them may be interconnected without invalid operation. (See Figures 5 and 6.)

System Operation

For the sake of clarity, I will explain the system operation in terms of a simple function of but two variables.

Consider the expression $a \wedge \smile b$. The operator would like to know for what assigned truth values of "a" and "b" the expression is valid, for what values it is invalid. The problem is introduced to the machine by means of the plugboard. Using patch cords, the operator connects one of the inputs of an "and" element to the variable generator output "a." To the input of a "not" circuit he links one of the "b" outputs of the variable generator. The output of the "not" unit is then connected to the other input of the "and" element. A cord is used to join the output of the "and" unit and the input of the amplitude discriminator.

With the throwing of the "operate" switch, the machine begins its automatic analysis. The variable generator sequentially assigns all the combinations of truth value to the variables, "a" and "b." Logically operating on these values, the elements representing the constants "not" and "and" produce a pulse pattern which varies as that function of "a" and "b" which is "$a < \smile b$."

After passing through the amplitude discriminator, which standardizes the pulse amplitudes, the pulse train is transferred to the cathode-ray display. Synchronized with the variable generator, this output device writes the truth table evaluation defining the expression "$a \wedge \smile b$." Because there are only two variables, the solution appears eight times. In other words, the truth values of "c," "d" and "e" have no effect upon the solution.

The simple example explained above serves to illustrate how the machine attacks much more complex problems involving more variables and much more intricate relations between them. (See Figure 17.)

The manner in which the machine handles a more complex problem is graphically represented in Figures 18 and 19.

The over-all operation of the machine's units is presented in a general flow diagram. (See Figure 20.)

Photographs of the machine are included to show construction and appearance. (See Figure 21.)

Projections

My reading in symbolic logic, its relationship to electronic switching systems and allied fields, as well as my recent investigations in these areas, indicate to me that there are many avenues open for interestingly new research. Some investigations in which I am currently engaged, as well as several of my ideas for future work, follow.

1) I am currently engaged in the development of electronic analogs for several of the more obscure logical functions.

2) I have begun work in the design of circuit elements which will enable my logic analyzer to operate on quantified propositions.

3) As a result of some rather recent further contemplation, a new system for the electronic solution of logical problems has come to me. I plan to further investigate this system which, through the use of a memory, features sequential, rather than simultaneous, truth evaluation.

4) Another area in which I hope to pursue some research is the application of symbolic logic to the analysis of graphical and pictorial data. I hope to relate this to electronic logic systems through the use of flying spot scanning techniques. I am especially interested in working on the problem of image recognition.

5) A rather recent development in symbolic logic is the multivalued logic, where the number of truth values that the variables may assume is greater than two. These systems have some very unusual properties, and it appears that they will be useful for such applications as the analysis of circuits containing various forms of nonlinear devices. I have done some preliminary work which leads me to believe that it will be possible to deal with these truth-value systems electronically. I hope to do work which will result in formulating the bases of a device for the electronic simulation and analysis of rectifier, and possibly saturable reactor, circuitry."

3

"An Investigation of the Packing of Convex Congruent Polygons" was part of the entry of Robert T. Moore of Silver Spring, Maryland, one of the winners of the Fifteenth Science Talent Search. Bob now has completed his undergraduate work in college and is beginning graduate study in theoretical physics. His summers have been spent at the National Bureau of Standards working on mathematical linguistics, artificial intelligence and information retrieval projects in the Data Processing division.

"Introduction

A study of the problem of the packing of convex congruent polygons is roughly analogous to a determination of the possible shapes that the pieces of a jigsaw puzzle may have if they must be alike, straight-sided and convex. The assembled puzzle is unbounded, and the number of polygons in it unlimited.

This problem is a special case of a larger one, the packing of polygons in general. . . .

I have investigated the special case first because it is sufficiently limited to make a solution conceivable, although even this is potentially a very broad problem.

A Topological Limitation

Fortunately the topological nature of networks makes the problem much more limited than it appears. On the basis of this nature of networks, as expressed in special cases of Euler's general formula for polyhedra and the Lebesgue-Brouwer "tiling" theorem, I proved the following limiting theorem.

Theorem I:　Convex congruent polygons will pack only if they have six or fewer sides. (See appendix I for proof.)

The problem is thus limited to four types of polygons: triangles, quadrilaterals, pentagons and hexagons.

The Oriented Cell Packing

To investigate the problem further it is necessary to formulate a method of proving whether or not a given polygon will pack. To serve this purpose I evolved and proved:

Theorem II:　Any convex polygon which alone or combined with congruent polygons forms one large polygon made up of three pairs of opposite sides, such that the members of each pair are parallel and congruent, will pack. (See appendix II for proof.)

This large polygon is often concave and thus at least one of its pairs of sides is made up of broken lines. Parallel, as used in this case, means that all the corresponding parts are parallel; and, combined with the congruency, means that the sides are translatable into one another without changing the orientation of the polygon; hence the name "oriented cell."

After having finished a good portion of this project, I learned that a proof of the oriented cell, somewhat simpler than mine, was evolved in crystallography research, using a non-cartesian coordinate system and vectorial sums in such coordinates. I am using mine, however, because it is my own work and it is proved by the plane geometry techniques with which I am familiar.

Subsequent work is further simplified by two corollaries:

Corollary A: The oriented cell packs as a hexagon made up of the vectorial sums of the parallel and congruent side pairs, such that these vectorial sums are parallel and equal. (See appendix III.)

Corollary B: A polygon with three pairs of sides such that members of each pair are opposite and properly congruent, and one pair parallel, is an oriented cell. (Properly congruent means that one member need not be turned on its back to be proven congruent to the other.) (See appendix IV.)

It might be noted that although it is possible to prove that all polygons covered by Theorem II and Corollary B will pack, and that those not covered will not pack *in an oriented way*, (see appendix V), it is not possible to prove that those not covered will not pack at all, without constructing a complete theory of the packing of concave polygons; and this last I leave to later years or wiser heads.

A Method of Deriving Polygons for Study

In order to study polygons and the manner in which they pack, it is desirable to develop a system, rather than to use mere random selection of subjects. The technique I have developed makes use of the fact that, in hexagon packings, exactly three polygons, thus three angles, must lie about any given vertex. Considering one vertex, there are seven sets of angle packings: (1) three successive angles about a point, (2) two successive angles and one alternate angle, (3) three alternate angles, (4) two like angles and a successive, (5) two like angles and one alternate, (6) two like angles and an opposite and (7) three like angles.

My approach has been to consider each of these sets by placing the three prescribed angles about a point, then determining various sets of side equalities necessary for this packing to be possible. For each set I found that there are eight cases of side equalities to be considered. In some cases, I have found that it is necessary to consider four intersection points instead of one, in order to prove that the polygons pack. These four may be considered in a snowflake pattern. (Appendix VI.) In several very stubborn cases, it is necessary to consider still more vertex intersections.

Classes of Packable Polygons

Using the techniques outlined in the last section, it is possible to generate packable polygons (if the technique is carried to enough steps). I have tried to place all of those generated in general classes, and have found and proved three.

The first packing grows out of Set 1 and is quite general. The hexagon considered has one pair of opposite sides parallel and equal, and two of these hexagons may be combined to form an oriented cell. All Set 1 hexagons are covered in this class. (See appendix VIIa.) It might be noted that if one unlimited side of this hexagon is of no length, a class of pentagons is generated. If the parallel and equal sides are both of no length, the class covers all quadrilaterals. If one of the sides of the quadrilateral is of no length, this class also covers all triangles. It is also the most general class, having a seven-fold infinity of polygons satisfying the conditions. (Appendix VII B.)

The second class of packings grows out of Set 2, and has one pair of opposite sides equal, the two sides adjacent to one member of the first pair also equal, and three particular angles adding up to 360°. Four of these make up an oriented cell. (See appendix VIII A.) It is a more limited class than Class I, having only a six-fold infinity of satisfying polygons, (appendix VIII B), and covers most of the Set 2 packings which do not fit in Class I.

The third class grows from Set 3, and has three separate pairs of adjacent sides equal, the angles included by these pairs of sides all equal to 120°. Three of these polygons make up an oriented cell. It covers two of the Set 3 cases, the others being Class I polygons. (See appendix IX A.) It is a very limited class, having but a three-fold infinity of polygons. (Appendix IX B.)

This completes the classes I have thus far proved.

Work Yet To Be Done

There is considerable scope for further study of this problem. I hope to complete the remaining studies as soon as possible. . . .

Possible Applications

If applications of this work are considered desirable, they may be found. In its three dimensional counterpart, this study is possibly relevant to crystallography and organic chemistry (high polymers) and may have applications to problems yet unposed. . . ."

The following appendices to this paper are included as examples of the proofs.

"Appendix I

'Theorem I: Convex congruent polygons will pack only if they have six or fewer sides.

Basis:

V=number of vertices (intersections of lines) in a packing.

E=number of edges.

P=number of polygons.

n=average number of vertices or sides per polygon.

Euler's formula for polyhedra applied to plane network, in any packing, $V-E+P=1$.

Lebsegue-Brouwer "tiling" theorem applied to finite sized polygons, in an unbounded packing, $V \leq \dfrac{nP}{3}$

and $E = \dfrac{nP}{2}$.

Prove: $n \leq 6$.

Proof:

1. $V-E+P=1$, $V \leq \dfrac{nP}{3}$, $E = \dfrac{nP}{2}$,

$\therefore \dfrac{nP}{3} - \dfrac{nP}{2} + P \geq 1$.

2. $\therefore 2nP - 3nP + 6P \geq 6$.

3. $\therefore -nP \geq 6 - 6P$.

4. $\therefore nP \leq 6P - 6$.

5. $\therefore n \leq 6 - \dfrac{6}{P}$.

6. In an unbounded packing $P \rightarrow \infty \therefore n \leq 6$.

7. In packings of convex congruent polygons, all polygons are the same, $\therefore$ the number of sides of the packing polygons must be six or less.

Appendix III

Corollary A: The oriented cell packs as a hexagon made up of the vectorial sums of the parallel and congruent side pairs, such that these vectorial sums are parallel and congruent. (See figure 2.) Note: The symbol "X . . . Y" should be read "the broken line connecting

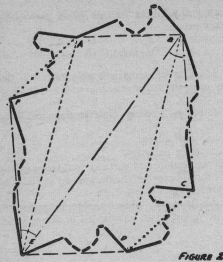

FIGURE 2

FIGURE 3

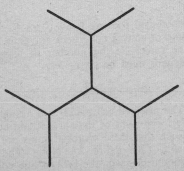

FIGURE 4

points x and y." "‖≅" means "both parallel and congruent."

Given: Polygon A . . . B . . . C . . . D . . . E . . . F . . ,
such that A . . . B‖≅D . . . E, B . . . C‖≅E . . F,
C . . . D‖≅F . . . A.

Prove: Hexagon ABCDEF has AB‖=DE,
BC‖=EF, CD‖=FA.

Proof:

1. A . . . B≅D . . . E, ∴ they may be superimposed.
2. By identity, AB=DE.
3. In the cell each component of A . . . B is ‖ and = to a corresponding component of D . . . E, AB is the vectorial sum of A . . . B, and DE is the vectorial sum of D . . . E, ∴AB‖DE.
4. ∴AB‖≅DE.
5. By similar method, BC‖=FE, CD‖=AF.

Appendix VI

In fitting three angles about a point (as in figure 3) a number of sets of side equalities may be derived. Each angle is included by two sides, thus there are three side pairs. Each of these side pairs may have two orientations (by turning the angle upside down in its space), thus the number of possible sets is 2^3 or 8.

At times the equalities thus derived, coupled with the information about side orientation gained from the angles (which must add up to 360°), are not sufficient to prove that a given polygon packs as one of the general classes. In this case, four or more vertices must be considered, normally in an arrangement such as shown in figure 4."

Chapter 9 • MEDICAL SCIENCES

1

BARBARA CONWAY OF Chattanooga, Tennessee, did a project on "Experimental Teratology" which won an American Medical Association award at the Tenth National Science Fair. Then she was invited by Dr. Hans Selye, world authority on stress as a basic cause of disease, to work during the following summer in his laboratory at the Institute of Experimental Medicine and Surgery at the University of Montreal. Not only was she the first American to have such an opportunity, but she was permitted to perform surgery herself.

"My next-door neighbor has a malformed little girl five years old who was born blind in one eye as the result of her mother's having a very bad case of flu in the second month of pregnancy. This started me thinking that if I could prevent only one case like this, it would be worth a great deal to mankind.

Early in the same year of 1957, when I was working on a science project entitled "Stress—Basic Origin of Disease," I read in the newspaper two very interesting articles regarding stress and cortisone as being causes of cleft palate and harelip in humans and mice. A little later my science club sponsor gave me an article on "Congenital Malformations" in the October, 1957, *Scientific American.* My exhibit therefore shows over a year's research on teratology. My objective is to find possible preventions by studying some causes in this new field of preventive medicine.

Teratology is a branch of science dealing with congenital malformations (deformities before birth). Heredity is not the only cause of congenital malformations; environment during pregnancy is also an important factor. This factor has not always been recognized. A few scientists, such as Stockard in 1921, were experimenting with this idea, but it was not generally recognized until after the 1941 epidemic of rubella (German measles). By "environment during pregnancy" is meant such things as German measles, deep anesthesia, X ray, long airplane flights, certain drugs, diet (vitamin deficiency), accidents and emotional tensions. Any of these environmental factors can affect the fetus.

Here are five possible precautions which can be observed during pregnancy as possible preventions of congenital malformations.

1. Some serious eye defects and Mongolism (retarded minds) may be prevented by controlling rubella (German measles).

2. Some blindness, Mongolism and cerebral palsy may be prevented by avoiding deep anesthesia (surgery and major dental work).

3. Various deformities may be prevented by avoiding X ray and long airplane flights (oxygen deficiency).

4. Some cleft palates, skeletal and internal defects may be prevented by paying close attention to diet (vitamin deficiency).

5. Some Mongolism may be prevented by close attention to pregnancies of older women.

This is a new field of preventive medicine called "prenatal pediatrics," which concerns unborn children in their mother's wombs.

I then began experimenting with pregnant white rats and mice.

Experiment I

One pregnant white rat was given 1 to 3 mg. of hydrocortisone for 14 days, from the sixth to the twenty-first day of pregnancy. On the twenty-first day of pregnancy she delivered 4 babies, 3 of which had malformations. There were 3 with undescended testes, and 1 of the babies with the undescended testes also had a malpositioned heart.

Experiment II

One pregnant white rat was shocked in the refrigerator twice, on the second and tenth days of pregnancy, for 8 hours at 38° F. On the twenty-first day of pregnancy she gave birth to 10 babies. As a result of this environmental factor 8 of the 10 babies were malformed, the rarest of which was a hermaphrodite, an animal which has both the male and female sex organs. This animal had 2 female ovaries and a uterus, and 2 male prostate glands. The proof of this is a pathology report from a well-known pathologist,

Dr. Jack Adams, of the Baroness Erlanger Hospital, Chattanooga, Tennessee. There were 5 babies with undescended
testes and 1 with a malpositioned heart. There was even a
liver which was diagnosed as "fatty degeneration of the
liver" by Dr. Jack Adams.

Experiment III

One pregnant mouse was shocked in the refrigerator for 8
hours at 38° F. for 2 days, on the sixth and thirteenth days
of pregnancy. On the twenty-first day she gave birth to 4
babies. One of these 4 babies had malpositioned testes.

Experiment IV

One pregnant rat was operated on in the ninth day of
pregnancy, December 23, 1957. In the operation I removed
amniotic fluid from 4 yolk sacs, attempting to cause congenital
malformations. During the operation she ceased breathing, but
I revived her by inhaling and exhaling through a rubber tube
held over her nose. About 13 days later she gave birth to 8
babies. As a result of this operation 3 babies were deformed,
1 with a malpositioned heart and 2 with malpositioned testes.

In 85% of rats the normal descent of testes is 18 to 31
days; the range is 13 to 51 days.

Experiment V

One pregnant mouse was shocked in the refrigerator at
38° F. for 13 days, from the seventh to the nineteenth day,
for from 1¼ to 4 hours. On the twentieth day, a day early,
she gave birth to 9 babies. In this litter, as a result of this
environmental factor, 5 babies were born with malformations
—2 with cephalhematomas (blood tumors of the brain),
and 1 with no skin covering his skull. These babies were
stillborn.

Experiment VI

The same mouse in another pregnancy with the same male
had no unusual environmental factor. As a result of this all
4 babies had apparently normal heads.

In conclusion I have shown that in four out of four cases,
where the pregnant female has been subjected to unusual
environmental factors, at least one of her litter has been

born malformed, and in one case where the same mother was not subjected to any unusual environmental factors, the litter was apparently normal.

In continuing my work I hope to discover preventions of congenital malformations which may be of great benefit to mankind.

Bibliography

D'Amour, F. E. and Blood, F. R., *Manual for Laboratory Work in Mammalian Physiology*, University of Chicago Press, 1956.

Griffith, J. Q. Jr. and Farris, E. T., *The Rat in Laboratory Investigations*, J. B. Lippincott Co., 1942.

Ingalls, T. H., "Congenital Deformities," *Scientific American* (Oct., 1957), 109-116.

Warkany, J., "Congenital Malformations," *Pediatrics*, Vol. 19, Part II, No. 4 (April, 1957), 719-792."

2

Diane J. Davis of Whippany, New Jersey, was a finalist in the Ninth National Science Fair. The title of her project was "Cancer Induced by the Rous Sarcoma Virus."

"What is cancer? What causes it? What preventatives and cures are there for this dread disease?

These questions confront many people today, and through my project I set about answering some of these questions for myself. I worked with two main problems. First, what is the latent period for tumor appearance in relation to the various dilutions of the virus which I used? Second, is there any histological difference in the structure of the invaded cells in relation to the virus dilution used?

Dr. Vincent Groupé and Dr. Raushner of the Rutgers Institute of Microbiology instructed me on proper laboratory technique and gave me directions for preparation of the Rous sarcoma virus extracted from tumor tissue by differential centrifugation. I made dilutions up to 10^{-5}, which are prepared in 10 steps by transferring 1.0 ml. of the 10^{-1} (4.3 ml.

saline, 3 ampoules virus extract) into 9.0 ml. of physiological saline solution. This then is a 10^{-2} or 1:100 dilution. To make the 10^{-3}, 1.0 ml. of the 10^{-2} is added to 9.0 ml. of diluent, etc. The placement of saline in tubes and the exchange of the virus solution from one test tube to another was done with 10 ml. and 5 ml. pipettes, respectively, under extremely sanitary conditions. Flaming of the tubes was important each time the plugs were removed to kill germs around the neck, burn up fragments of cotton from the plug and keep a steady stream of hot air moving outward from the bottles, which prevented germs from entering. Because of the code "if in doubt, throw it out," many pipettes I used while learning the technique of sanitary transfer of solutions were discarded, including the solutions within them. This technique, like others, is mastered through practice.

On completion of the virus dilutions, I was given fifteen white Leghorn chicks and eight white Beltsville turkeys, all one day old, for inoculation with the virus. Five normal chicks and one normal turkey were added to the final grouping. With the help of Dr. Raushner, I tagged each bird in the right wing web and then injected 0.2 ml. of the virus diluent into the left ventral subcutaneous tissue through the *extensor carpi radialis* muscle to prevent leakage. I divided the chicks into groups of 5 and inoculated all in each group with either 10^{-1}, 10^{-3} or 10^{-5} virus diluent. The turkeys I placed into groups of 4 and used 10^{-1} and 10^{-3} virus diluents.

For about the first month, I raised the chickens and turkeys in my bedroom, because of the need for a constant warm temperature. Each day I checked all the birds for tumor appearance and growth, and kept accurate records of all the data acquired.

The first tumors appeared on January 22, in three chicks and three turkeys. Two thirds of the tumors developed from the 10^{-1} and the other third from 10^{-3} virus diluents. One chick died from head lacerations caused by the pecking of other chicks. Two turkeys were so badly pecked that I put them in separate brooders until their wounds healed. I made the first sacrifice on January 24 of a bird with a +2 tumor growth (the degrees of classification of tumors by their size ran from +1, which is a group of small growths about the size of a pinhead, to +4, which is usually by then just one huge, hemorrhaging mass of malignant cells) and placed the tissue from the wing web into Zenker's fluid, which I had mixed the previous night. I found no metastases in any of the internal organs. The following day I sacrificed another bird, obtaining the same results.

On the morning of January 25, I visited the Morristown Memorial Hospital to observe a pathologist making slides. I learned proper procedures and a few tricks for quicker and better results in making my own permanent slides.

On February 5, I again visited the Morristown Hospital, this time with my own processed tissue. The stains haematoxylin and eosin were used in the final steps. Observation under the microscope showed definite invasion of the striated muscle tissue by the cancerous cells.

Upon dissection of a chicken February 8, I found widespread metastases in all the organs. Although later I also found metastases in other birds, it was more common for the birds to die before reaching this advanced stage of cancer.

One bird, injected with a -3 diluent, developed what appeared to be a huge tumor at the sight of injection. When three weeks later the growth had entirely receded, I wrote Dr. Groupé and received a probable answer to the problem.

. . . . It is a rather common occurrence that when a a tumor becomes contaminated with certain but not all bacteria, that tumor for an unknown reason may disappear to all intents and purposes.

Another bird, although nothing appeared in the wing web, died of cancer in the head, which possibly developed because of cancerous tissue eaten by the chicken. Dissection showed that the tumor had progressed from the left eye to the throat and had closed the gullet, preventing the bird from eating.

Because after a certain age chickens develop a resistance to the Rous sarcoma virus, no birds with the -5 diluent showed signs of tumor growth. It was therefore unnecessary to keep the birds any longer; so on March 15 all the remaining chickens were killed, leaving only a few turkeys, who were slow in developing their tumors. However, I did section a part of each wing web at the spot of injection and sent the tissue through the regular process for slide making.

To finish the last procedures in making my slides, I went to the National Institutes of Health in Bethesda, Maryland, where I became acquainted with Dr. Albrecht. He advised and helped me in the final analysis of the tissue under study. A center of growth dominated most of the slides, showing signs of deterioration. Both striated and smooth muscle fibers were affected by the invading malignant cells. The 10^{-1} growths showed an increase in activity as compared to the 10^{-3} tumors. There was, however, no apparent difference as far as cellular structure was concerned.

Average Latent Period	Virus Dilution
7 days	10^{-1}
9 days	10^{-3}"

3

"A Study of the Effect of Tranquilizers on the Metabolism of White Mice" was presented at the Ninth National Science Fair by finalist Asa William Bennett of Washington, Georgia.

"I first became interested in experimenting with tranquilizers in October, 1957. A summer issue of *Scientific American* discussed methods of assembling apparatus for determining metabolic rate in mice, and about the same time public interest was aroused concerning the effects of new tranquilizer drugs on the human body. It was revealed that some doctors were using the drugs quite freely and that the total effect of these drugs had not been thoroughly tested experimentally. I decided that an experiment to determine the effects of the drugs on metabolism might give valuable information concerning the over-all function of tranquilizers. Many questions began to enter my mind. Do tranquilizers have any effect on metabolism? If they do, is the effect a secondary one resulting from nervous system synaptic interference, or is there cellular level metabolic interference? The last two questions I could not check experimentally, but the first one I could check, and perhaps find information which those who are trained in medical science might use in exploring the other two areas more fully.

My next steps were concerned with collecting more reference material, setting up apparatus for determining metabolic rate, obtaining experimental animals and drugs and learning to run accurate tests.

With the exception of a beam balance, all equipment used in my experiment was home-assembled. Cages for white mice were built from orange crates and screen wire. Five flasks, a Mason jar and an aspirator were connected by glass and plastic tubing. Definite amounts of either calcium chloride or soda lime were placed in the respective flasks to serve as absorbers of water vapor and carbon dioxide. A water faucet was fitted with an adapter for the aspirator.

Wyeth Laboratories generously donated a supply of two recently developed tranquilizing drugs. Dr. Duggan, a local physician, gave me a 5-cc. vial of promazine hydrochloride, and several syringes. A medical student, Mickey Standard, gave much assistance, both with information on the drugs and in preparing (with local hospital facilities) a 30-cc. vial of meprobamate.

On December 4 I made the first trial run. My figures indicated that the metabolism of the mouse tested was 1.21, an impossible figure. Normal metabolism in mice ranges from .72 to .97. A total of fourteen runs was made in December. All showed incorrect metabolic rates, some too high, many too low. Finally I located a cause of the inaccuracy. My beam balance had a dull knife edge and was giving erroneous weights, which ranged from one tenth of a gram to as much as one gram. New, highly sensitive triple beam balances were purchased, and tests recommenced January 15, 1958. Still no normal metabolic rate could be obtained. I then observed that much water vapor exhaled by the mouse was condensing on the walls of the animal chamber. The body heat of the animal was causing the temperature inside the chamber to be higher than that on the outside. An electric heating pad (low temperature) thrown loosely over the animal chamber raised the temperature of the outside walls and solved the problem. No more condensed water vapor! Once these difficulties were overcome, I consistently obtained metabolic rates which fell within the normal rate, .72 to .97. I was then ready to inject tranquilizers and make comparisons. Reading had helped me to formulate a hypothesis concerning expected outcomes.

In several scientific publications, I found that both meprobamate (Equanil) and promazine hydrochloride (Sparine) act on the central nervous system, but are classed neither as stimulants nor depressants. Promazine is said to exert "narcobiotic" action on subcortical areas of the brain, and to control overt motor and verbal activity. It is also believed to inhibit certain metabolic functions of living cells, particularly those of the nervous tissue. Meprobamate seems to act on the interneuronal circuits as a blocking agent and to have a selective effect on the thalamus. High doses have been known to produce subcortical and cortical changes. Meprobamate also relaxes the voluntary skeletal muscles and modifies the number of incoming stimuli. All references show that a relaxed state follows an injection of either meprobamate or promazine hydrochloride. These findings led me to assume that I might expect both drugs to produce an appreciable decrease in the total metabolic rate of my mice.

In testing this hypothesis, I have made 107 metabolic runs since the first test of December 4, 1957, and have found that the tranquilizers, meprobamate and promazine hydrochloride, produce a lowered metabolic rate in white mice. The average decrease following meprobamate injection is 13% in males, 14% in females. In the case of promazine hydrochloride the average decrease is 12% in males and 15% in females. Excitement caused by a placebo injection of physiological salt solution produced a 9% increase in both males and females.

The slowdown in metabolism may be even greater than experimental results indicate, because the injection of physiological salt solution produced a metabolic increase. A physiological salt solution is not in itself irritating or stimulating to the animal body, so the excitement or nerve tension must have been caused by the needle entering the peritoneal cavity. In tranquilizer injection there was needle involvement and the lowered rate may represent a drop from the needle-excited rate rather than from the normal rate.

Tranquilizers administered to human beings may not have as much effect on metabolism as this experiment indicates for mice. The therapeutic human dose is proportionately smaller than the dose given to experimental mice and the metabolic effect may be proportionately smaller.

Since general metabolism is definitely lowered by meprobamate and promazine hydrochloride, there may be cellular level action of the drugs as well as nerve impulse interference. However, I did not have the equipment necessary to test this theory, so I will leave that for someone else.

With my project I have been extremely fortunate. I received a trip to the National Science Fair at Flint, Michigan where I placed fourth in the boys' biological sciences category. A fourth award carries with it a gift of $25 worth of scientific equipment. This and the tremendously educational experience of the National Fair makes me feel well paid for my 300 hours of work. I can never adequately express my gratitude for the assistance and encouragement I received. The inspiration of my teacher, Miss Dorothy Wright, has been of inestimable value in helping me carry on this project."

4

Lynda Wallace of Cheyenne, Wyoming, now a student at Creighton University, Omaha, Nebraska, was one of the forty top winners of the 1958 Science Talent Search. As part of her winning entry, she submitted her report on an unidentified bacterium she had discovered. Her tests showed that the enzyme or product given off by this bacterium liquefied carbohydrates and proteins.

Lynda's science teacher and sponsor, Sister Mary Paulinus, requested and received the first grant ever made by the National Institutes of Health for a research project to be carried out by a high school science club. The high level of their laboratory work and the exciting results of their study of the bacterium, which the club members have christened "Lynda," has drawn national attention.

In September of 1959 the story of this search for a fast-acting anticoagulant which may have important use in treating coronary thrombosis was detailed by James M. Liston, well-known writer and editor, in a major article for the American Medical Association publication, *Today's Health*.

A summary of Lynda's paper, "Tentative Identification and Further Studies of an Unknown Bacteria," is presented here.

"In December, 1956, I began work in bacteriology. At first I was interested in it chiefly as a class project. However, a flask of potato agar was left unsterilized in a laboratory closet for a few days. After this time I found that large gas bubbles had been formed in the agar. To see if any change would occur in it, I decided to leave the agar in the closet and observe it. At the end of a week the agar was completely liquefied. My objective then became the identification of this bacteria, which differed in its properties from most other types in that it was capable of liquefying agar.

During the following months I ran several tests described in the *Manual for the Pure Culture Study of Bacteria* concerning identification. My tests and results were based on a period of 24-hour growth at 20° C.

I tentatively arrived at this identification:

Kingdom:	Plant
Phylum:	Thallophyta
Class:	Schizomycetes
Order:	Eubacteriales
Family:	Pseudomonadaceae
Genus:	*Mycoplana*
Species:	*bullata*

In the hope that something may eventually be found to keep potatoes from spoiling during storage, tests were also run to determine the effect of antibiotics on this species of bacteria. Those used were Polymyxin B, Chloromycetin, penicillin, Viomycin, Streptomycin and Neomycin. All these antibiotics were contained on a small tab which was placed on a pour plate. It was then noticed after forty-eight hours of growth that Neomycin and Streptomycin had inhibited growth, while Polymyxin B, Chloromycetin, penicillin and Viomycin had not. These last four antibiotics even seemed to encourage growth, but no direct proof was obtained and the study is still to be pursued.

Recently an article in *Scientific American* described a number of experiments by the California Institute of Technology concerning the effect of coconut milk on the growth of plants. Potatoes were among those being tested and because of the peculiar reaction of this bacteria on potato agar began to make tests concerning the growth of the bacteria in coconut milk, and on potatoes grown in coconut milk. The coconut milk seemingly contains one of the prime factors for cell growth.

At present I am using dilutions of coconut milk. The dilutions are from 1:10 to $1:10^{12}$. Each solution of coconut milk was inoculated and after growth compared to growth in an equal amount of nutrient broth. This comparison was accomplished by means of plate counts to determine if growth advantages could be secured by the use of coconut milk.

When this investigation was initiated the need for running a combined nutrient-coconut milk broth was not apparent but this study will have to be made.

An interesting phenomenon occurs in the coconut milk cultures which will be referred to by their key, 10^7, 10^8, 10^9 and 10^{12}. Growth decreased in direct proportion to the dilution in the first six cultures, as is consistent. In the 10^7 dilution there is practically no growth, if any at all. But the 10^8 dilution immediately shows an increase almost equal to that of 10^1 and 10^2. Growth in 10^9 again decreases almost to the point of no growth. Gradually small amounts of growth then begin to appear until growth in 10^{12} is almost equal to that of 10^8. These results were so startling that several runs were made. The results are recorded in the table below.

	1	2	3	4	Average
$1:10^1$	640	680	598	652	642
$1:10^2$	576	524	590	564	563
$1:10^3$	524	546	490	520	520
$1:10^4$	396	389	440	420	386
$1:10^5$	228	236	264	251	245
$1:10^6$	70	70	81	92	78
$1:10^7$	22	22	40	30	29
$1:10^8$	411	450	420	408	422
$1:10^9$	67	56	59	61	58
$1:10^{10}$	232	214	230	280	239
$1:10^{11}$	316	360	370	380	356
$1:10^{12}$	517	560	520	650	561
$1:10^{13}$	51	32	70	75	58
$1:10^{14}$	103	112	120	123	114

With such interesting developments I have also begun to determine the effect of bacterial growth on potatoes in another manner, again employing coconut milk. This time, however, I have begun to grow sets of potatoes from seedlings. One set is grown in coconut milk, the other in water as a control and comparison. From these potatoes I will determine the growth factor of coconut milk on potatoes and later I will take the potatoes grown in this manner, prepare them as a medium and inoculate them with the bacteria and compare the growth on this media with that of the regular potato agar and coconut milk solutions.

As the odor produced by this bacteria has proved so challenging and mysterious, I am initiating research on its isolation and identification also. Seemingly it is not the bacteria which causes the agar to liquefy but some product which is

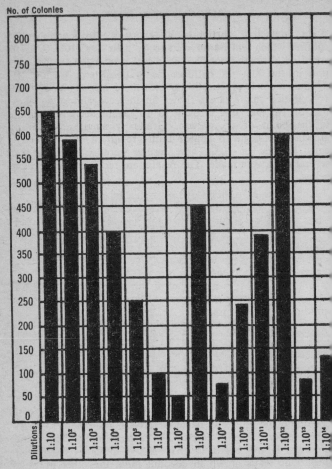

GRAPH SHOWING
INCONSISTENT
GROWTH OF BACTERIA
IN COCONUT MILK

formed when a particular substance is utilized as food—probably a protein, as is indicated by liquefication of nitrate agar, gelatin, potato agar, bean agar and coconut milk.

Summary

1. Tests were run on an unknown bacteria, which causes agar to liquefy, according to the methods described in the *Manual for the Pure Culture Study of Bacteria* and it was tentatively identified as *Mycoplana bullata*.

2. Preliminary studies of the relationship of this bacteria to antibiotics show it inhibited by Neomycin and Streptomycin, but uninhibited or even encouraged by Polymyxin B, Chloromycetin, penicillin and Viomycin.

3. Work with growth of this bacteria in coconut milk shows an inconsistent rise in a dilution of $1:10^8$ and $1:10^{12}$.

4. Comparison of growth in coconut and nutrient broth shows coconut milk alone. to be less good. The need for further study on a combination of coconut milk-nutrient broth medium presents itself.

5. Seemingly it is a product of the metabolism of the bacteria which causes the agar to liquefy. Isolation of this product is still in progress.

Bibliography

Bergey, D. H., Breed, R. S., Murray, E.G.D., Hitchens, A. P., *Bergey's Manual of Determinative Bacteriology*. The Williams and Wilkins Company, Baltimore, 1939.

Difco, *Manual of Dehydrated Culture Media and Reagents for Microbiological and Clinical Laboratory Procedures.* Difco Laboratories, Detroit, Michigan, 1948.

Frobisher, Martin, *Fundamentals of Bacteriology.* W. B. Saunders and Company, Philadelphia and London, 1952.

Edited by the Committee on Bacteriological Technique of the Society of American Bacteriologists, *Manual of Methods for Pure Culture Study of Bacteria.* Biotech Publications, Geneva, New York, 1946.

Salisbury, Frank, "Plant Growth Substances," *Scientific American,* 197: 125-134, April, 1957."

5

David R. Brown of St. Louis Park, Minnesota, did a

project on "Humeral Transplants." It won him the top American Medical Association Award at the Ninth National Science Fair, as well as several other awards. Three years later David became a top winner in the Nineteenth Science Talent Search.

"Introduction

To the zoologist, anthropologist, anatomist and orthopedic surgeon it is important to know to what degree the shape and size of bone varies due to its own method of growing and the posture action of muscle. Actually a considerable amount is known, by those who have grown early skeletal tissue in glass (tissue culture) and also by those who have transplanted early embryonic bones into a nonmuscular membrane in the chick egg. However this tells us only about very early stages and in general has shown us chiefly that bones (before true bony tissue appears) do not need a normal environment to develop their basic shape and size.

It would be important to specialists to know if growth will continue indefinitely in an outside environment. If there are only differences in growth and development, what are the factors responsible? The only way to solve this is to transplant bones of newborn animals to nonfunctional locations. This has been done by several investigators.

To study this matter of growth development and to see how certain tissues survive transplanting, a member of the Department of Anatomy at the University of Minnesota has been working with the mouse, placing small bones under the skin. This technique has answered many questions, but a certain slowing up of the blood supply has been noted. The blood supply of a growing bone, by its rate and volume, determines the rate of growth and makes possible the appearance of bony tissue itself.

Whether a rich blood supply is more normal may be tested by the relatively simple process of putting the bones of a newborn mouse into the circulatory system of a chick egg.

The egg is a possible site, because of its rich blood supply and because antibodies are not being produced in the egg. Growth is also limited by the time the blood starts circulating and by the nineteen-day shutoff. The only possible time for transplanting is between nine and nineteen days. Ten-day growth in the egg is being compared with ten-day growth in the mouse, because the age of implant in both cases is fourteen-day embryonic (birth—seven days). This age is chosen because growth is rapid at this stage.

Obtaining the Humeri

a. The uterus of a fourteen-day pregnant mouse is opened and the embryos removed.
b. The embryos are then placed under the dissecting microscope and the humeri removed.
c. These bones are then placed in saline solution for a short time while the series is being collected.

Placing the Bone in the Mouse

a. The hair is removed from the side of an adult mouse and an incision about 1 cm. long is made.
b. A humerus is then placed on the underlying membranes to grow.
c. A cover glass is then placed in the incision to retract the opening and to make observation possible.
d. The wound is allowed to heal, causing the window to adhere to the surrounding tissue.

Placing the Bone on the Chorioallantoic Membrane

a. Exposing the chorioallantoic membrane
 1. A small square is cut in the shell of a living egg.
 2. The shell is then lifted and the surrounding tissues are removed.
 3. The chorioallantoic membrane is now exposed.
b. The humerus is now placed on the membrane.
c. A cover glass is then placed over the membrane to replace the shell, and sealed with paraffin.
d. The egg is then placed in the incubator at 103-105° F. and a relative humidity of 60%.

Results

Normal 2-day (control)—4.95 mm.
Subcutaneous transplant (mouse)—4.50 mm.
Chick egg transplant—5.16 mm.
 The above figures are the results obtained from an average of all the grafts. The period of growth in all cases is ten days, during the fourteen-days embryonic to two-days postnatal interval. The average size of the bone at transplantation was 4 mm., ranging from 3.85 mm. to 4.1 mm. in length.

Conclusion

I find that my original hypothesis (as stated in the introduction) is conclusive. The possibilities of these techniques in medical research are unlimited. For example, the method of observation employed through the use of a cover glass allows the worker to observe the ossification process, as well as other tissue growth, quite readily. The application of other forms of tissues upon the chorioallantoic membrane is a coming technique. I have thought of using the parathyroid hormone with the subcutaneous transplants in the mouse and seeing the effect of rapid calcium metabolism on the bone. The introduction of acetic acid compounds into the blood stream may produce decalcification of the transplanted bone. The study of dentation through the transplantation of fetal mouse mandibles is now being done at the University of Minnesota."

6

An excellent project that was thoroughly researched won honors for Sheila Marie Most of Gulfport, Florida. Her "Modern Science in Dentistry" was selected by the American Dental Association as one of the two most outstanding exhibits in dental science at the Tenth National Science Fair. The purpose of her project was to contrast the condition of the teeth of a prehistoric people with the condition of teeth today, examining the prehistoric and modern diets and taking into consideration the advantages of modern medicine and dentistry. Sheila and Mary Sue Wilson, the other winner, were honored guests at the ADA Centennial Convention in New York in September. Sheila was selected for the second time to represent the Pinellas County Science Fair, St. Petersburg, Florida, as a finalist at the Eleventh National Science Fair-International, where she again won a First Award given by the ADA.

Sheila says, "Now, along with my interest in archaeology is a strong turn toward dentistry, and my future plans are to enter the field of dentistry. . . . Members of the American Dental Association have greatly assisted me with knowledge unattainable through any class or text. . . . I know that neither money nor anything else could have bought the education that the National Science Fair and the Dental Association meetings have given me."

For her project, Sheila used a great variety of information sources, which she lists in detail at the end of her research paper. The following is an abstract of her project report.

"Findings

While reconstructing aboriginal Timucuan Florida Indian skulls and jaws (1000-1200 A. D.) excavated by the exhibitor, a complete lack of dental caries in each and every jaw was noted, although these Indians suffered other dental defects. . . .

These conditions led to research into diet habits of such Indians to determine the reasons therefor and to contrast the effects of their diet on their teeth with the effects of a diet of today on our teeth.

Discussion

Diet habits of the Indians were controlled by what nature provided seasonally. Foods consumed were:

Meats:	Deer—most important	Raccoon	Beaver
	Bison (early times)	Boar	Squirrel
	Fox	Wildcat	Manatee
	Alligator	Skunk	Otter
	Panther	Muskrat	Snake
	Opossum	Rabbit	Turtle
Fowl:	Turkey	Duck	Sea Birds
Fish:	Local varieties	Oysters	Scallops
	Mollusks	Clams	
Vegetables:	Corn (Maize) main staple		
	Pumpkin	} all three cultivated	
	Beans		
	Wild Roots		
Fruits:	Wild Plum	Cherry	Swamp
	Crab Apple	Persimmon	Chestnut
	Blackberry	Huckleberry	

Tobacco was used. (Swanton, 1922, pp. 357-362)

In winter, they subsisted largely on fish and game, which were cooked on wooden racks placed upon forked stakes over a fire, then smoked and dried for storage. Note: The predominant Indian head type has exceptional bony ruggedness of face and mandible attributed to their marine diet, which was extra rich in phosphates. (Hrdlicka, 1922)

Much grit, remaining in the Indian's staple food—corn— after grinding, had a tremendously abrasive effect on their teeth, causing severe wear. This, in turn, exposed the tooth's nerve, causing it to shrink away. Often the tooth abscessed and, if severe, this sometimes led to death.

Smoking of meats and fish to preserve them tended to toughen the meat. Chewing these foods also caused severe wear. Many female jaws showed the results of chewing leather for softening purposes.

Although it is impossible to determine if gingivitis and Vincent's infection were present, evidence of pyorrhea, abscesses, malocclusion, poor alignment, tartar deposits and stains, impaction plus loss of teeth by diseases were much in evidence in almost every jaw.

Present twentieth century diet is usually a matter of personal choice. Most foods are available all year round with the fairly recent development of frozen foods, plus modern transportation. Vitamins, taken on medical advice, help make our proper food and vitamin intake the best in the world. In addition, we have the advantage of many dairy products.

Today, modern parents protect their children's health (before and after birth) and their own with all modern scientific medical and dental aids made available to them. Somewhere along the line, *refined sugars* (i.e., candy, pastries, candy-coated gum, soft drinks and ice cream) creep into the child's diet—an unnecessary but highly palatable addition. In 1830, the United States per capita consumption of sugar was 12 pounds per year, and we consume *100 pounds per year* per capita.

This tremendous increase in our *refined sugar* consumption leads to the conclusion that refined sugar is largely responsible for our high national rate of tooth decay. The frequency with which sweets are eaten is an even more important factor than the amount consumed. Continued and repeated acid attack is more dangerous to the teeth than occasional attack.

A typical modern family of father, mother and daughter (exhibitor's family), who availed themselves of full dental and medical care, shows the following defects:

Father: missing—3 third molars
            fillings—9

          partial dentures—2 to replace maxillary right and
          left second bicuspids

Mother: missing—8 (4 third molars due to impaction;
                  maxillary left second bicuspid, first and
                  second molars, right second molar)
          fillings—30
          partial denture—1 to replace maxillary left second
                bicuspid, first and second molars
          crowns—2 mandibular right first and second
                molars

Daughter: (deciduous)—missing 1—maxillary left central
                incisor nerve killed in blow in accident,
                subsequent abscess, extraction at age
                4½
          fillings—4—numerous pinpoint caries remaining
                unfilled at dentist's discretion
          (permanent)—missing—none
          fillings—21
          orthodontic treatment to correct separation and
          straighten overlap of maxillary incisors

The hardest part of the human body is the tooth. Teeth remain intact after death long after the bones of the skeleton have turned to dust. Yet, they are among the perishable parts of the body during life because of dental caries. Figures for the United States show:

2-year-olds—50% have 1 or more carious teeth.
6-year-olds—have 3 or more carious deciduous teeth.
16-year-olds—have 7 decayed, missing or filled teeth. (Less
              than 4% of this age group have remained free
              from dental caries.)

Summary

It will be noted that in the Indian diet, there were only natural sugars consumed. Therefore, although they had no knowledgeable control over their many dental troubles, they escaped dental caries.

Conclusion

The following care, plus the reduction in the large quantity of refined sugar-containing foods, would show a marked improvement in America's dental health.
1. Regular visits to the dentist, starting at about age 2.

2. Brushing after every meal may help prevent a certain amount of caries. (Commercial tooth powders and pastes are pleasant to use, but have no special virtue in cleaning. Many dentists recommend finely precipitated chalk or bicarbonate of soda as safe and inexpensive.)

3. Removal of tartar and other deposits and stains once or twice a year by dentist.

4. Treatment by orthodontist for malocclusion and improper alignment.

5. Use of fluoride applied directly to teeth by dentist or taken internally through properly treated drinking water (usually 1 part fluoride to 1,000,000 parts water).

Experiments at Grand Rapids, Michigan, after 5 years of fluoridation, show caries reduced 66% in permanent teeth of 6-year-old children. Communities with no central water system can have children's teeth treated with applications of fluoride by a dentist on eruption at ages 3, 7, 10 and 13 years."

7

Mary Susan Wilson, Cedar Falls, Iowa, was one of the top American Dental Association winners at the Tenth National Science Fair. Her project, "Bacterial Resistance to Antibiotics," is described below.

"Introduction

The purpose of my project was to develop two strains of bacteria: *Staphylococcus aureus* (pathogen) and *Sarcina lutea* (nonpathogen) with resistance to penicillin. Having accomplished this, I tested these mutant strains against other antibiotics (Bacitracin, Achromycin, Aureomycin, Terramycin, Streptomycin, Dihydrostreptomycin, Triacetyloleandomycin and Ilosone) which normally inhibit their growth and observed the effects of these antibiotics on the above organisms. I obtained the pure strains of the two types of bacteria from a bacteriological supply house and transplanted cultures from these two strains. My family physician furnished the antibiotics used in this project.

Procedure

I used a fairly new method in obtaining the mutant strains

of bacteria. Metal slants were made on which to place the petri dishes, as shown in Diagram I.

Nutrient agar was prepared for growing bacteria. I poured one slant consisting of 30 ml. nutrient agar and let it solidify. Then, I placed the petri dish on a level surface and poured a second slant of agar mixed with a standard solution of penicillin and let it diffuse for twenty-four hours. The required gradient of concentration results as the penicillin in the top wedge diffuses into the bottom wedge. The final preparation is pictured in Diagram II.

Originally, I planned to use this procedure throughout the project but as the work progressed, I used other methods.

In working with the nonpathogens, I used two methods. I poured all of those dishes by the wedge method but used different inoculating procedures. The first method was as follows: I sterilized a flask with 150 ml. of sterile distilled water. After cooling the water to body temperature, I inoculated the water with the organism by using a platinum loop and mixed thoroughly. I poured this solution on the prepared petri dishes and incubated them for forty-eight hours. I noted that the growth of bacteria extended about halfway across the dish from the end of least concentration. As the gradient of concentration of antibiotics became greater, the colony count per square centimeter became less. I assumed that those colonies growing in the highest concentration from that test were mutations. I took the colonies that grew in highest concentration and transplanted them, as described previously, to a petri dish of identical preparation. After incubating this for forty-eight hours, I observed that the growth had extended completely across the dish. The results of these tests are summarized at the end of this report.

In the streak method I used the same preparation of agar but a different method of inoculation. With a platinum inoculating needle, I made six to eight streaks from the end of least concentration extending across the petri dish.

I incubated the dish for forty-eight hours, after which I noted that the streaks extended about one fourth of the way across the petri dish. I took the colonies from the outermost ends of these streaks and transplanted them to a dish of identical preparation. After forty-eight hours of incubation, I noted that the streaks had extended about three fourths of the distance out. In each test I used four petri dishes, transplanting each time to four more. The preliminary results with this method indicate that the organism was developing resistance to the antibiotic. I did not work extensively with this method; therefore, I am not presenting data at this time.

In investigating *Staphylococcus aureus*, I used three procedures. I initially tried the water method (as described earlier) with the wedge preparation of agar. I used sterile conditions because *Staphylococcus* is classified as a pathogenic bacteria. When grown on nutrient agar, the organism becomes less virulent. However, I used the standard procedure for handling pathogens to avoid contamination. This method proved to be inadequate, and I abandoned it.

Then, I used the streak method (described above), but this also proved to be unsuccessful as I was not proficient in the method at that time.

I finally used the filter disk method. I poured 25 ml. of agar into a sterile petri dish, using a platinum loop to inoculate the unsolidified agar with the organism. I allowed this preparation to solidify, placed a prepared filter disk containing penicillin in the center of the dish and allowed this preparation to incubate for forty-eight hours. I noted that the organism grew in a circle about 1.5 cm. from the filter disk. Assumption: Bacteria growing nearest the disk are resistent to the antibiotic and therefore mutant. I then transplanted the colonies from the innermost edge of the circle to a dish identically prepared. I incubated this for forty-eight hours and noted that the circle of inhibition had diminished. I took the innermost colonies from this test and transplanted them to a dish of similar preparation. It was noted that in this test, the *Staphylococcus* grew completely to the disk. This indicated that the organism had developed resistance to penicillin. The results of these tests are summarized at the end of this paper.

As my work progressed, I found that I would need a procedure by which I could get an accurate count of the colonies. I designed and built a colony counter as shown in Diagram III. I was able to use this counter with the tests using *Sarcina lutea*.

The initial upper wedges were prepared, using a standard solution of 200,000 units of penicillin plus 25 ml. sterile distilled water. After testing this solution, I found that the organisms were completely inhibited by this concentration, so I proceeded to dilute the solution by adding 50 ml. water for each test. I finally found that 200,000 units of penicillin in 800 ml. sterile distilled water were adequate for the growth of bacteria.

In testing the mutant strains of *Staphylococcus* with other antibiotics, I poured 4 petri dishes with 25 ml. of agar. After inoculating the dishes with the mutant strain of bacteria, I placed a prepared antibiotic (Streptomycin, Ilosone, Bacitracin, Aureomycin, Terramycin, Triacetyloleandomycin and Dihydrostreptomycin) in the center of the petri dishes and incubated them for forty-eight hours. The results taken from the tests with *Staphylococcus* are given at the end of this report.

I used the wedge method in testing the resistant strains of *Sarcina lutea*. I used Achromycin, Aureomycin and Terramycin, making a standard solution of each, the same concentration as the penicillin solution.

The dishes were prepared in the same manner as used in testing the organism with penicillin. I used the water dilution procedure for inoculating.

In order to make a quantitative determination of the mutation rate, it is necessary to determine the number of colonies developing at each level of antibiotic concentration. The information would be more meaningful if the count included the colonies that would develop in a given region but would not develop in a region of greater concentration of the inhibiting agent. The following procedure was devised to obtain this count statistically.

The grid on the colony divides the petri dish into regions, each 1 cm. wide, starting with the least concentration in strip 9. The average number of colonies per square centimeter for each strip is determined by counting the number of colonies in each square centimeter. The strips are divided into square centimeters by the grid. Counting is done at a number of places along the strip to obtain an average number per centimeter for each strip. The colonies counted per square centimeter is the actual count. Let this count in each row be designated by the letter A followed by the number of the row. In Row 1 this would be designated by A1, in Row 2 by A2, etc. To determine the number of colonies that could develop in a given strip but not in a strip of greater concentration, some simple statistical calculations are required. Let B represent the number of colonies that could grow in a given strip, but not in one of greater concentration. $A1 - A2 = B1$, $A2 - A3 = B2$, etc. These results have been graphed by assigning B an index number. This was done in the following manner. B1 was assigned the number 100. Therefore, $B1/100 = B2/X$. By finding X in each case, the given B is assigned a number. The strip numbers 1 through 9 constitute the other axis of the graph.

While working on my project, I came upon some results that I felt were interesting, but because of lack of time I was unable to pursue them. My work was dealing primarily with organisms resistant to antibiotics, therefore I was surprised to observe that one of the antibiotics (Achromycin) inhibited the mutant strains of *Sarcina lutea* to a greater extent than the nonmutant strains. This would be an interesting aspect of the subject for further study.

Results

1. A mutant strain of *Staphylococcus aureus* was developed and resistance to penicillin was evident.
2. The mutant strains of *Staphylococcus aureus* were tested against other antibiotics (Aureomycin, Terramycin, Dihydrostreptomycin, Bacitracin, Streptomycin, Ilosone and Triacetyloleandomycin).
   a. The mutant organisms showed resistance to Bacitracin, Terramycin and Triacetyloleandomycin.
   b. The mutant organisms were not resistant to Ilosone, Dihydrostreptomycin, Aureomycin and Streptomycin.
3. Mutant strains of *Sarcina lutea* were developed. Resistance to penicillin was evident.
4. These mutant strains were tested against Aureomycin, Terramycin and Achromycin.
   a. The mutant strains were not resistant to any of the above antibiotics.

Summary

This work is an illustration of the evolutionary process that is continually going on in all forms of life. As unfavorable conditions arise, these organisms must change in order to survive. Thus, the development of effective antibiotics is a never-ending task. Antibiotics today may be ineffective tomorrow, because of changes in the organisms.

This study has been and is of great importance from the medical and clinical standpoint. The effective use of antibiotics to combat infection depends upon their ability to inhibit all strains of a given species of bacteria.

The ultimate antibiotic would be one which would completely inhibit the growth of a given disease-producing organism, and against which the organism could not successfully mutate.

Bibliography

Epstein, *Miracles from Microbes*, Rutgers University Press.

Greaves and Greaves, *Elementary Bacteriology*, W. B. Saunders Company.

Irving and Herrick, *Antibiotics*, Chemical Publishing Company, Inc.

Pratt and Dufrenoy, *Antibiotics*, Lippincott.

Scientific American, October, 1954, "The Structure of the Hereditary Material," by F. H. C. Crick.

Scientific American, November, 1956, "Transformed Bacteria," by Rollin D. Hotchkiss and Esther Weiss."

1

MARY-DELL MATCHETT, Hinsdale, Illinois, decided that telescope making should not be an exclusively male province. Here is a report of her ambitious project, "Construction of an Eight-Inch Cassegrainian Telescope," which helped her to become one of the top forty winners in the Fifteenth Science Talent Search.

"Introduction

Amateur telescope making is not merely a hobby or an interest—it's almost an obsession. There is a satisfaction in it that nothing else can quite equal. Perhaps it is the high degree of accuracy—the near-perfection—required that gives this sense of satisfaction to even the rank novice; or perhaps it's just the remoteness of the interest from all else. Whatever the cause, there *is* something intriguing about mirror making. Apart from its being a science, a skill and a sport, mirror making is an art.

The Geometry of Telescoptics

If a spherical mirror is struck by light rays radiating from its center of curvature, they will be radii of the sphere and will be reflected back to focus on the center. Since a circle is actually an ellipse whose conjugate foci coincide, let one focus move away from the mirror and it becomes elliptical; rays from either focus will still converge upon the other. Again move this outer focus out all the way to infinity and our ellipse reaches its limit: the parabola. *A parabolic mirror, then, will reflect rays from one of its foci, infinity (parallel rays), to the other at a finite distance from the mirror.* As we increase the parabolic mirror's finite focal length, the concavity of the mirror decreases; when this second focus reaches infinity, the mirror is plane. Now if we don't know any better and move this focus beyond infinity, lo and behold! It has traveled all the way around the universe [1], for it

1. This makes a nice story. Technically, the plane mirror has a virtual focus at infinity behind itself as well as the real one in front.

now appears at a finite distance *behind* the mirror, while the second appears at a finite distance *in front of* the mirror. The surface of the mirror is now convex and its curve is the limit of the parabola: a hyperbola. Obviously the mirror cannot bring the rays from the finite focus in front to a *real* focus behind itself; it actually causes the rays to diverge as if *from* this focus. This is, then, not a *real* but a *virtual* focus. Conversely, *the hyperbolic mirror can reflect rays from its virtual focus (i.e., converging as if upon it) to its real focus at a finite distance from itself.*

Now let's apply this to the Cassegrainian telescope (Figure II). A parabolic mirror reflects the light rays from one of its foci, infinity (the distance to a star being relatively infinite), to the other, finite, one, F. This focal point must, however, be moved back to the eyepiece behind the primary, so these converging rays are now intercepted by a hyperbolic secondary mirror, which reflects them from its virtual focus, F, to its real focus at F'.

The Cassegrain system obviously decreases the angle at which the converging rays meet, giving us the effect of a longer focal length without lengthening the telescope tube. (This is very convenient if you don't want to have twelve feet of telescope on your hands.) A long focal length is desirable because the magnification of a given eyepiece is directly proportional to the effective focal length of the mirror system.

The Primary Mirror

"Eight Inch," my primary mirror, was almost completed before I gave a thought to making her a Cassegrain. The caption, "How to Make a Cassegrain (and why not to)" in *Amateur Telescope Making* was an open dare. I took it. The single adaptation necessary was the perforation of the primary. This is cut by a cylindrical metal surface rigged on a drill press.

I'll skip over the strong arm work of grinding the mirror, except to mention the principle involved. When equal glass disks are ground one upon the other, the upper hollows and the lower becomes convex. This occurs because, at the extremity of the stroke where greatest pressure is brought to bear, the center of the upper disk and the edge of the lower bear the brunt of the abrasive effect.

Polishing, again, is largely strong arm work — but this time the principle is a bit more complex. In fact, there is some disagreement on the subject. The mirror is polished against a viscous lap of pitch. According to the theory *I* accept, the tiny flakelike particles of the polishing agent sink into the pitch lap, producing a surface of tiny razor edges that shear away minute layers of glass. The ultimate result is an optical surface, entirely free from pits and scratches.

Figuring the polished mirror is the hurdle that separates the men from the boys. By special polishing strokes the mirror's curve is first brought to a segment of a perfect sphere, then deepened ever so slightly to a perfect parabola-of-revolution (on about the fiftieth try). An optical test enables us to "see the mirror's exact figure." For Foucault's test we stand the mirror on edge and, at the center of curvature (displaced to the left very slightly), we place a pinpoint of light. The rays diverging from this point are radii of our sphere and are all reflected back to the center of curvature (displaced equally to the right, where we may see them). At this focal point we allow a knife edge to cut the cone of light rays. As we look along the knife edge at the mirror, if the sphere is perfect, we see the entire surface shadow out evenly and simultaneously, since all returning rays pass through the focal point and are cut off. If an area of the mirror is too deep to be a part of the sphere, its focus will be in front of the knife edge and the knife edge will cut a shadow on that area, moving in a direction opposite its own. Conversely, if the area is too shallow, the shadow will move in the same direction as the knife edge. The parabolic mirror gives a computed variation in focal lengths of zones between the center and edge of the mirror. These variations are measured with great accuracy by a micrometer adjuster on the knife edge. This test is, incidentally, so delicate that the heat generated by an onlooker's body causes the light pattern to shimmer, so that the tester cannot interpret it. When the elusive parabola is finally perfected, the Newtonian maker's troubles are over—and the Cassegrain maker has just begun to fight.

The Secondary Mirror

I decided to make the effective focal length only 3.3 times the actual focal length (38 inches), for a longer e.f.l. gives greater power but smaller field. Computations for size and placement of the secondary are shown in Figure II.

Rough and fine grinding are the same routine as before, ex

cept that this time we use the convex bottom disk. The curve of a hyperbolic mirror is so far from a sphere that it is more practical to test it during the polishing process and correct as we polish. Since the secondary is convex, Foucault's test is useless; we must make a special testing mirror and use a different test. The setup is shown in Figure IV. The testing mirror is a spherical Cassegrain whose radius equals the primary's focal length, 38 inches. If we placed a pinpoint of light at its center of curvature, we would get rays reflected back at the same angle our primary mirror produces, and we could use these to test the secondary. Since inserting the secondary would cut off the source of light, we must place our light at the other focus of the system—behind the hole in the testing mirror. Now when our pinhole light is displaced slightly to the left, we can use the knife edge displaced to the right to see whether all rays are converging upon the desired focal point, and can correct accordingly. After much exacting work and—let's face it—a bit of luck, we at long last wind up with a secondary that works in perfect conjunction with our primary.

Reflections

There is as much to learn about the why and how of a telescope as about its uses. A year ago I had never even looked through a telescope. The first I ever used was my 4¼-inch Newtonian, "T. Ela Scope." It probably cost me more to build her than it would have to buy her—but I don't care. You'll never believe it unless *you* have made your own telescope, but it is every bit as fascinating to make the telescope as to use it.

A Note of Thanks

There are times when the telescope maker feels a most irrepressible urge to drop a brick on his mirror. At such moments, the influence of fellow workers (a twisted arm) is pure salvation. Thanks, then, to the other "inmates" of the Adler Planetarium's Optical Shop for restraining me.

My greatest debt of all, however, I owe to Mr. A. V. Shatzel, Assistant Director of the Adler Planetarium—for not laughing at the little ignoramus who said she was going to make a telescope. I've learned more optics from him than from any or all the books I've ever read.

Bibliography

Ingalls, A. G. (Editor). *Amateur Telescope Making, Book I.*
    Scientific American (Pub.)
Thompson, A. J. *Making Your Own Telescope.* Sky Publish-
    ing Corporation.
Mr. Shatzel (the aforementioned). (He's not really a book
    —just sort of a library.)"

2

"A Solar-heated Greenhouse" was the project that Robert
Kirk Seaton of Elizabeth, New Jersey, entered in the 1958
Science Talent Search for the Westinghouse Science Scholarships and Awards. In the paper that helped Bob to become one
of the top forty winners, he says:

". . . .The essential problem was to find a way to collect
heat energy from the sun, store it and release the energy as
needed to heat the plant-growing area.

The greenhouse I designed is composed of two parts: a
heat-gathering and storage unit and a plant-growing chamber.
The heat-collecting unit is of the flat-plate type (Figure 1).
It is composed of 2 panes of glass separated by ¾-inch
air space; this is the most efficient separation distance. Behind
the glass is a large sheet of aluminum foil painted black. Glass
is relatively permeable to heat of short wavelengths as is
contained in the sun's radiation. However, glass is opaque to
the longer wavelengths of heat such as are radiated by comparatively cool objects. The wavelength radiated is inversely
proportional to the temperature of the radiating body.

The heat of short wavelength passes through the glass
and is converted to heat of long wavelength by the aluminum
foil. Thus the heat is trapped behind the glass. The heat is
then transferred by radiation and by convection currents from
the blackened foil to the storage unit, located immediately
behind the collector plate. Air is allowed to pass through the
space between the glass and the foil via slots at the bottom
and top of the foil. In the storage unit, the heat is picked up
by 1-gallon black metal cans containing water, a method
chosen because of its high specific heat, its cheapness and its
heat of fusion at 0°C. These cans have a capacity of 1120

pounds of water and can be stacked loosely enough for the air to circulate around them.

Since I wished to limit the size of the greenhouse base to 4 by 3 feet and still have my plant area on top of the maximum size, it was necessary to have the plant chamber hang over the collector plate. However, this overhang was designed so that it would not shade the collector plate during January, the coldest month of the year. As spring advances and less heat needs to be stored, the overhang shades more and more of the collector plate. In the fall the situation is reversed.

With masonite construction insulated with 3-inch Fiberglas batting, the heat loss can be calculated to be about .12 B.T.U.'s per square foot per degree difference per hour. This value takes into account the masonite and glass surface areas in the completed greenhouse. Then, using the formula $Ht = AU(T-TO)$, where

Ht—heat transmitted per hour in B.T.U.'s

A—surface area in square feet

U—over-all transmission per hour per square foot per 1° F. difference

T—inside temperature

TO—outside temperature,

I calculated that 4030 B.T.U.'s will be lost, assuming a minimum maintained inside temperature of 40° F. and an outside temperature of 0° F. and a 14-hour night.

I wanted my collector plate to be able to collect about 3 times the heat lost during a 14-hour night. This leeway would allow for a 2-day supply of heat in case of cloudy weather. Therefore, I wanted my plate to collect about 13,090 B.T.U.'s during a clear day. I used the formula $\dfrac{A\,(S\text{-}L)\,(m)}{C} = $ B.T.U.'s collected per day, where

A—collector area in square centimeters

S—the solar constant of 1.94 calories of heat falling on each square centimeter of a surface perpendicular to the sun's rays per minute

L—loss due to glass absorption

m—collection period in minutes

C—conversion rate of calories to B.T.U.'s to compute the area of the plate.

I figured on a loss of .94 calories per square centimeter due to glass absorption and reflectance. I also figured on a maximum collection period of 6 hours. Solving this equation for

A (the area), I arrived at 9300 square centimeters for my collector-plate area. I therefore designed my plate to be 10 square feet in area (9280 square centimeters).

The collector plate is inclined at an angle of 60° so that the sun's rays fall perpendicularly on it during the coldest weeks, affording maximum collection and penetration.

During the day, the heat is collected and stored in the cans of water. At night, when the temperature of the air around the cans becomes less than that of the water within the cans, the stored heat is radiated from the cans and warms the air around them. This warmed air, being lighter, rises to the top of the storage unit, where it can be admitted through dampers to the plant chamber.

The plant chamber is 4 feet wide and 3 feet deep. The roof slopes from the rear to the front. The height in the rear is 11 inches and in the front 4 inches.

The framework is composed of 2-by-3-inch pine and the walls are of waterproof masonite. The model is made so that it is entirely collapsible, each surface being built as a prefabricated panel. All the panels are held together by bolts.

With a few structural alterations this design could be made into a large walk-in model. Once set up and running, the heating bill would be nothing. . . ."

3

"The Behavior of Soap Bubbles and Films" was reported by Arthur T. Winfree of Stamford, Connecticut, one of the winners in the Nineteenth Science Talent Search.

"Introduction

This project began, ludicrous as it may seem, as a one-weekend effort to make a nonpopping soap bubble; and what it has thus far mushroomed into is well over a pound of abbreviated notes, graphs and equations on the chemical and physical properties of soap films.

A great deal of the research up to now has resulted not so much in concrete answers as in the development of a group of more tractable, specific questions. So this paper attempts to give a representative sampling of both experimental results and the further experiments and calculations they have suggested; a descriptive or qualitative summary is to be found in the text and the 35-mm. slides, with more precise information located in the appendix.

Chemistry

If any one thing was vital to this phase of the project, it was unquestionably my notebook, in which *everything* seen or done in the lab was recorded. I recorded in special detail those things that seemed unusual, confusing or contradictory. Thus, any time I thought I'd explained some irregularity, I was able to look months back for observations with which to confirm or discredit the new theory.

The first several weeks in the lab were spent investigating, first, various bath soaps in aqueous solution, then, finding these most unsatisfactory, pure and mixed stearates at various concentrations and temperatures. Even these were no better than commercial solutions for film strength and stability at room temperature.

Among the multitudes of other things tried were wood rosin, oleic acid and polyvinyl alcohol (PVA); these three proved to have some particularly remarkable properties, the most important of which I list here.

1) Wood rosin, digested with 4.4% NaOH solution, forms mobile red-brown soap solution which, while incapable of blowing bubbles, can form small films which dry *without popping!* (See photos 6 and 10.)

2) Alkali salts of oleic acid, at 1-5% concentration in water, form soap bubbles and films of surprising color and stability (which I also learned later from C. V. Boys); NTE (nitrilo-triethanol) oleates as 1-2% solutions form films that last for days on end and are at most about 1000Å thick! Ammonium oleate, 1/5%, is similar, but greater concentrations are quite viscous.

3) PVA, while reducing the stability of liquid films, makes strong, perfect dried films *and bubbles* possible. By using a low molecular-weight grade of PVA, saturating the solution with sucrose and working in dry air, I've been able to produce soap bubbles so strong that they can be taken in hand and squeezed until they pop! I hope to improve this solution by the addition of a nonhygroscopic liquid plasticizer and a PVA-insolublizer.

Planned are a few syntheses, notably of abietic acid esters and double-bond addition compounds of oleic acid and the rosin acids, to produce water-soluble additives for special-purpose films, but only one has been performed to date.

Surface Physics

The most significant physical property of soap films is their surface tensions (about 30 to 35 dynes./cm.), which causes their surface areas to be minimized under the conditions imposed (with a few exceptions in which the area is only a relative minimum). Thus the film between two parallel wire rings is a catenoid, because a catenoid has the least area of all such imaginable surfaces.

Another characteristic of films is that nowhere in a stable foam (as I was delighted to see under the microscope) will a place be found where more than three films intersect in a line, or more than four lines (six films) intersect in a point. Consequently, all intersections must be at a 120° angle. I've not yet been able to show why these things must be, but I am working on it.

I've made some progress in analyzing soap-bubble systems by making the assumption that where other forces resist the minimization of surface, the total potential energy of the system (gravitational, pneumatic, etc.) is minimized. However, the proof that this assumption is generally valid depends on the solution to an equation which I can't solve yet.

Maxwell proved that a cylindrical bubble will become unstable when its circumference equals its length, but, once again, I haven't completely shown why. I've outlined a proof which includes the more general case of surfaces of revolution, and it will be complete the same day the differential equation mentioned above is solved. In the meanwhile, a proof based on the minimum-energy assumption is feebly progressing.

The other major lines of work in this department have been 1) an investigation of the geometric properties of multibubble systems (see Fig. B), and 2) a mathematical study, to be confirmed in the lab when complete, of the possibility of making a stable doughnut-shaped bubble. I think it's impossible, but a conclusive proof also depends on the problematical differential equation.

General Physics

Perhaps the most striking fact about oleate films is their

brilliant color, caused by interference of light waves at the film's surface. However, the question arose whether this interference was due to the thickness of the entire film or to a monolayer of some sort on the film's two surfaces, and I collected a good bit of experimental evidence for each hypothesis. The monolayer idea was finally discarded and all the data was correlated without it. This means soap films are only 1000 to 10,000Å thick.

An interesting aspect of soap-bubble physics, and one which is well suited to experimentation in the home lab, is the collapse of a spherical bubble through a controlled orifice (see Fig. C). The graphed results agree closely with the predictions in slope, but the Y intercept is about four times too large; the shape of Graph B may have been influenced by the extra curvature of the long orifice tube used. Bubble weight apparently had no significant effect on collapse rate.

It has been demonstrated (e.g., by Boys) that some gases pass rapidly through a film by osmosis, yet I've never seen equations about it. So I'm getting ready to determine the three constants in my general prediction, using gas-filled acoustical lenses made of soap films. The plans and calculations are almost complete.

The fifth series of tests performed consisted of stretching a flat horizontal film in the open air, while feeding it with an eye dropper. Using statistical methods on the results of about 200 single tests, I found 1) that the maximum diameter of a plane circular horizontal film, beyond which it cannot support its own weight, is close to 10 inches, and 2) that the addition of about 30% glycerol (suggested by Boys) does substantially strengthen open-air films. Other experiments indicate that it retards evaporation, but at the same time reduces a film's ability to produce local variations in surface tension, T.

My principal instrument for studying liquid soap bubbles (as opposed to those which, containing water-soluble gums, are stable when dry) is the bottle, shown in Slide 16. I've used it for investigating the effects of chemical proportions on film characteristics, studying film physics through color patterns and gradually increasing the life span of a bubble from twenty minutes (early October) to more than fifty hours (late November).

The next major physical experiment planned (to precede osmosis tests) concerns surfaces of revolution, using the apparatus shown in Fig. D. In one kind of test, for example, let $r_1 = r_2$; attach ring 2 to the bottom of a measured bubble below ring 1 and note how far it falls when released. Knowing h, d, W, V, the weight of ring 2, and the bubble's original volume, one can find the surface, volume, potential energy, curvature and internal pressure of the bubble.

A further occasion for some interesting math and experiments is the behavior of the thin sticky threads which can be drawn from a Type E solution of 2% ammonium oleate — the surface forces tend to increase while the center of gravity of the thread seeks the lowest possible altitude.

Something I've recently begun at least to think about is the transmission of low voltage AC through soap films of various contours (tried DC—it electrolyzed the soap). By varying the contour, or causing the membrane to resonate, some surface integrals could be generated which might be of interest in analog computers.

The same goes for reflected light beams; the reflection from a catenoid film, for example, would give hyperbolic trigonometric functions.

One further possibility for an unusual study is growing bacteria or molds in a PVA-type film; their growth would be in two-dimensional space of almost any desired shape."

4

Brett Nordgren of South Bend, Indiana, top scholarship winner in the Sixteenth Science Talent Search, helped to construct an accelerator, then built an automatic Wilson cloud chamber to go with it. His report was presented in chronological order, outlining work begun two years before. The text contained a table, eight figures and four photographs. A bibliography was appended. Here is an excerpt from his work, "An Automatic Wilson Cloud Chamber."

"My cloud chamber began as a companion project to a one-megavolt Van de Graaff accelerator, constructed two years ago by a group of science students, including myself.

I plan to record phenomena occurring in the lower energy ranges with particles from our accelerator. The cloud chamber will make the paths of these particles visible for photographic study.

In general, cloud chamber research has been concentrated

in the area of very high energy particles, to the neglect of lower energies. Some low-energy phenomena of particular interest which I should like to study are electron pair production, proton capture and transmutation, and gamma-ray effects, such as the Compton effect and photoejection of electrons.

Even though subatomic particles are invisible, their vapor trails in the cloud chamber are visible and can be photographed and studied. To form these trails in my unit, a quantity of argon gas, saturated with the vapor of a 75% ethanol and 25% water mixture, is expanded to 1.08 times the original volume in a time of the order of 0.01 second. The resulting sudden cooling effect supersaturates the argon. When a particle passes through, ionizing the argon atoms in its path, the ions formed serve as condensation nuclei for the vapor. This creates a cloud trail along the path of the particle. These tracks must be quickly photographed, since within one second they will diffuse and vanish. Argon at two atmospheres with the alcohol-water mixture (as recommended in *Electron and Nuclear Physics*—Hoag & Korff) was used in my chamber because of the greater specific ionization and the reduced expansion ratio over other combinations. The optimum expansion ratios for various combinations of gas and vapor are given in Table 1.

After the picture is taken, the chamber is restored to its original condition by recompressing the argon and allowing it to "rest" for ½ to 1½ minutes to dissipate the heat of compression. During this rest time a potential of 100 to 500 volts is maintained through the chamber to remove all ions formed during this part of the cycle. This prevents them from fogging up the chamber during the sensitive time. Of course, this voltage must be removed just before expansion so that the tracks to be studied are not prevented from forming.

The cloud chamber proper (shown in Figure 1) consists of an aluminum cylinder 3 inches high and 6 inches inside diameter with ⅝-inch-thick walls. The top of the cylinder is covered by a ¼-inch-thick lucite disk, through which the pictures are taken. This window is held in place by an aluminum ring bolted to the end of the cylinder. The bottom of the cylinder is sealed by a ⅛-inch-thick rubber diaphragm separating it from a lower cylinder 1½ inches high. Compressed air is admitted to the lower chamber and then

MECHANICAL DETAILS OF THE CHAMBER

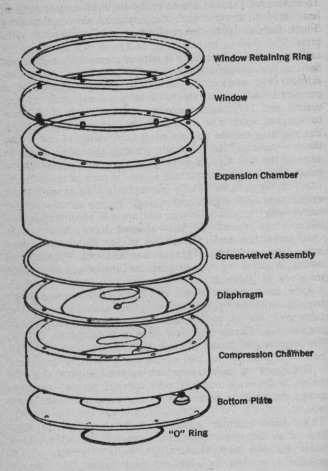

Window Retaining Ring

Window

Expansion Chamber

Screen-velvet Assembly

Diaphragm

Compression Chamber

Bottom Plate

"O" Ring

Figure 1

released after a suitable interval, causing the diaphragm to drop and thereby expanding the gas within the upper cylinder. To reduce the expansion time to the required 0.01 seconds or less, air in the lower chamber is released suddenly through a 3-inch-diameter port, covered by a thin aluminum valve plate. The plate is locked in place (as shown in Figure 2) until expansion is to occur. It is then released by a solenoid. Several other designs for this release mechanism were considered (Figure 4), but this system was chosen because it permitted the valve plate to have the least mass of any system and the solenoid needed to exert very little force to trip the valve. Due to the force of the compressed air tending to open the valve (15 psi, exerting 121 lb.) and the low mass of the valve plate mechanism (.17 lb.), the valve opens rapidly when released and allows the air to exhaust in a very short time.

When the chamber is to be recompressed, a pneumatic cylinder of my own design (see Figure 3) raises the valve plate and seals it firmly to the port. The valve is then locked in place and the cylinder drops away. . . .

In the design and construction of the cloud chamber, I have come to several conclusions. Although a magnet is useful in deflecting the particles to measure their energy, mass and charge, in much experimentation it is unnecessary. I considered using an electrostatic field to deflect the particles but this would have to be on the order of 1000 V. per cm., causing ionization problems. In the future I should like to try using a transparent disk-shaped plastic magnet recently developed, to be placed just below the window in the chamber. . . .

One major modification which may be attempted in the future is the addition of counter control; that is, a particle passing through the chamber will trigger a counter tube which will, in turn, trip the chamber quickly before the ions disperse. This method is generally used to record the tracks of cosmic rays. For this system, a quicker method of actuating the valve will become necessary, possibly one in which a DC solenoid, normally energized, is de-energized by a reverse pulse from a condenser. This produces very rapid action.

Design of the chamber is completed and construction is complete with the exception of the following items: camera mount and winding equipment; addition of several maintenance ports for filling the chamber with gas and for the possible insertion of radioactive sources; wiring of electrical connecting cables between the chamber and the control unit; and hookup of three solenoid air valves.

The chamber will be tested with the accelerator during Christmas vacation, when I shall have access to this machine. . . ."

5

Many unusual research problems were investigated by the winners of the Nineteenth Science Talent Search. A mysterious "spook" light caught the interest of young scientist William E. Underwood of Carthage, Missouri. In his paper, "Hornet 'Spook' Light Using the Double Refraction of Light Theory," he wrote:

"Last summer, I traveled twelve miles southwest of Joplin, Missouri, to a lonely road of northeastern Oklahoma, and here I first viewed the famous Hornet "Spook" Light. Even though the light had baffled all comers, including the U. S. Corps of Engineers, it was an immediate challenge to my curiosity. I shall endeavor to summarize briefly my investigation of this light phenomenon.

The Light

The case history of the light begins with observations made by residents in 1903. It appeared on some property near the state-line road now called the Original Spook Light Area. (See Appendix, Figure 1.) The light appeared self-luminous and its course was limited to a swampy draw filled with decaying vegetation. Because it bore the appearance of a lambent flame and was visible only when conditions were right, I think its origin was phosphoric, and its nature that of an *ignis fatuus* (will-o'-the-wisp). This display no longer exists.

In 1946 the U. S. Army Corps of Engineers performed a test on another light on a road which has come to be called the Old Spook Light Area. The results of this test have been best described by the State of Missouri Resources and Development Division, which stated, "They came away baffled." The Army test was conducted on a road approximately one mile north of the road from which the light is seen today (called the New Spook Light Area) and had no connection whatsoever with the present Spook Light.

My investigation concerns the present light.

On my first visit with friends to view the phenomenon, we parked on a gravel road at the top of a long slope. Soon after dusk, a suffused glow appeared in the sky to the west, over a range of hills. The center of the lighted area was in a line with the axis of the road. The greenish-yellow ball appeared to descend out of the hills and rapidly advance toward us. When we moved any distance toward the light, it would disappear.

Its maneuvers were of two types, the first being to vary in intensity, time of appearance, distance and often to become duplex. The second and less frequent display was yet more of a *coup de théâtre*. The light approached the observer and seemed to envelop him. But when he turned toward the east to observe its continuance, nothing was seen.

Refraction Theory

When a ray of light passes from one substance to another of a different density, it is bent out of its course, or refracted. The law of refraction is: When light passes from a rare to a dense substance, it is bent in the direction of a line that is perpendicular to the surface of the refracting body; when light passes from a dense to a rare substance, it is bent away from a line perpendicular to the surface of the refracting body. Furthermore, while light of all wavelengths travel with the same velocity in empty space, the velocity in material substances is different for different wavelengths. This effect is known as *dispersion*. The ratio of the velocity of light in a vacuum to the velocity of light of a particular wavelength in any substance is called the *index of refraction* of the substance for light of that particular wavelength. (See Appendix.) The index of refraction of a gas increases uniformly as the density of the gas is increased.

The index of refraction is also defined as the ratio of the sine of the angle of incidence to the sine of the angle of refraction. (See Appendix.) The index of refraction for any two media is constant, no matter what the angle of incidence.

Problem Analysis

My first concern was the light's customary remoteness. I rendered the ocular determination of its maneuvers more perceptible through a telescope. A 4¼-inch objective telescope was operated, using eyepieces giving magnifications of 40x, 90x and 200x.

Photographic resolution was poor because of the vibration of the telescope mount, air disturbance and natural movement of the light. (See Appendix, Figures 4 and 5.)

By using the telescope I was able to resolve as many as eight pairs of lights, the intensity of the Spook Light depending upon the intensity of the pairs of lights and the number of lights in the field of view. Upon taking into consideration the inverted image in the eyepiece, I was able to discern pairs of red lights to the right of the yellow lights, the red lights growing dimmer as the yellow lights became brighter.

Occasionally the light, as seen through the telescope, appeared as a flame which was green at the bottom and red at the top. I remembered that the light of sealed beam head lamps is polarized vertically. The wavelength of green light (5200Å) is shorter than that of red light (6500Å) and green light is refracted through a greater angle. These facts are consistent with the observations if the light is refracted.

Another important experimental fact is that equal amounts of radiant flux of different wavelengths do not produce visual sensations of equal brightness. Therefore, if a source gave off blue light as well as other light, it is likely the light would appear green, yellow or red.

Further reasoning led me to think that the cause of the light lay in the refraction of automobile head lamps from a road in direct line with the gravel road where I stood.

The fact that the light did not always appear substantiated the refraction of light theory in that if the light was bent, it would come down at different points and with various intensities, depending on the temperature and humidity of the atmosphere.

I put together a composite map of the area and decided that a section of Highway 66, running east and west from Commerce to Quapaw, Oklahoma, was in a direct line with my two observation points. I also noticed that Spring River crossed the area between the gravel road and the highway.

Water gains and loses heat much slower than cement or earth. Temperature and vapor content of the air above water vary as a function of the water's temperature. The temperature relationship of land to water would vary with: (1) season (water being given off by foliage in summer and water temperature varying from summer to winter), (2) changes from daylight to dark and (3) sudden atmospheric changes. Warm moisture-laden air is less dense than cool drier air and therefore a beam of light traveling from Highway 66 to an observation point on the gravel road would suffer two changes of direction—from dense, to less dense, to dense. This effect is called *double refraction* of light.

The average summer and winter temperatures for this area are 72° and 37° respectively, the night temperatures varying somewhat. By making several assumptions I have been able to calculate the indices of refraction of the different media and to approximate the refraction pattern for summer and winter. (See Appendix, Computation 2.)

The wattage of most sealed beam head lamps is 50/40, the head lamp having two filaments for bright and dim. Each car is equipped with two of these, their individual candle power rating being approximately 50/35. The intensity of the light at the point of observation would be a function of the inverse square law and the number and distance of the pairs of lights on Highway 66.

Experiments

Assuming the lights of the Old Spook Light Area and New Spook Light Area to have a common origin in automobile head lamps, even though their source was on a different road, I proceeded to carry out an experiment somewhat like the Army Engineers Test. (See Appendix, Figure 1.) Observations were made at points A and B on the map and the number of cars traveling the section of the highway between Commerce and Quapaw was recorded at point C. The intensity of the light was directly proportional to the number of cars traveling in an easterly direction. The reddish glow of the light would vary directly with the number of automobiles moving in a westerly direction. When there wasn't any traffic on the highway, it was possible to educe the presence of the light by flashing an automobile's head lamps at point C; the flashes were observed at point B.

Using a spectrotelescope I constructed, I found that the Spook Light had a continuous spectrum, such as an incandescent light has. If the light had been a luminous gas under atmospheric pressure, it would have produced a bright line spectrum. Thus the spectral pattern serves as a proof of an artificial incandescent source, such as an automobile's head lamps.

I took some infrared films of the light to see if it gave off infrared rays, but the roll of film did not develop.

Future Plans

Further study will require a modification of my photographic equipment to include color slides and infrared film, as well as to improve resolution. The telescope and camera mount should be made more sturdy to avoid disturbing the image.

I plan to get photographic proof of the light's continuous spectral pattern and this will require the addition of a film carrier to the spectroscope. I may also notice absorption lines near 7600Å from oxygen in the atmosphere.

A photometer calibrated in lumens and used in correlation with the telescope could be used to calculate the theoretical distance of the light.

A Recapitulation

The points upon which I base my conclusion that the Spook Light is the double refraction of automobile lights are: (1) In a telescope the lights are seen as pairs of white and red lights, (2) the actual angular width of these lights compares favorably with their theoretical angular width, (3) sealed beam head lamps are polarized vertically and the Spook Light is refracted light polarized vertically, (4) it was possible to control the actions of the Spook Light and (5) the physical features of the area support the theory.

Bibliography

Dull, Charles E., Metcalfe, H. Clark, and Brooks, William O. *Modern Physics*. New York: Henry Holt and Company, 1955.

Hodgman, Charles D. *Handbook of Chemistry and Physics*, Fortieth Edition. Cleveland: Chemical Rubber Publishing Company, 1958.

How to Use Your Telescope. Barrington: Edmund Scientific Company, 1959.

Kennom, Leslie G. *State of Missouri Division of Resources and Development*. Jefferson City: State of Missouri, 1946.

Sasuga, John. *Photocells and Sun Batteries*. El Segundo: International Rectifier Corporation, 1955.

Sears, Francis W., and Zemansky, Mark W. *College Physics*. Cambridge: Addison-Wesley Publishing Company, 1956."

6

"Thermoelectric Cooling" was the project presented by Frederick A. Moore, Rockville, Maryland, at the Tenth National Science Fair. Here is an abstract of his paper.

"Not a new phenomenon, thermoelectricity has been known since 1823. Seebeck discovered that electric currents are generated in a closed circuit made up of two different metals when the junction between them is heated. In 1834, Peltier, a French watchmaker, observed cooling (the absorption or generation of heat depending on the direction of the current) at the junction between two different metals.

The Seebeck effect has been used for a long time to measure temperatures with thermocouples, but thermoelectricity for power generation or for cooling was considered impractical until 1929. At that time, a Russian, A. F. Joffe, outlined the advantages of thermoelectric generators made of semiconductors. Active work was begun about ten years ago at the Institute for Semiconductors in the U.S.S.R., and great advances made.

The advantages of semiconductor thermoelements over metals lie in the fact that they can be made with high thermoelectric power and high thermal resistance. Metals tend to leak heat back through the bars so fast that they are impractical for power generation or cooling.

This experiment was undertaken to investigate the commercial possibilities of semiconductor thermoelectric cooling devices and power generators using c.p. or analytical grade chemicals and an inexpensive, commercially feasible process. Most of my experimental work has been done with modified bismuth telluride, and to do so, I developed a plating process using gold, which I believe to be original. Using this process, I have obtained very good results.

With present rapid developments of thermoelectric technology in the United States, several commercial devices will be marketed within the next two or three years.

Several envisioned devices using thermoelements are: 1) a portable hostess cart; 2) a clock-controlled baby bottle refrigerator and warmer; 3) a portable combination picnic refrigerator and stove operating from the cigarette lighter of a car; 4) perpetual thermoelectric power for space satellites; 5) a ten-mile-square section of Arizona desert covered with good thermoelectric generators which would generate enough electrical power for the entire United States, have no fuel costs or radioactive waste problem and practically no maintenance costs; and 6) a portable power generator heated by a stove or fire, which would run a TV set, electric lighting system and refrigerator, for camping or life in remote areas."

1

"A Method of Obtaining a Complete Balance of Life within a Closed System" was the ingenious project of Richard P. Bentley of Tupper Lake, New York. It was exhibited at the Tenth National Science Fair.

"The following is a report on the method by which I propose to maintain a complete balance of life ecology within a closed system. This experiment is important because the method could be put to practical application on long-term space flights and in submarines to eliminate the large area of space required to store food and oxygen. It would be of great value in any situation where food supply, oxygen supply and waste removal had to be self-contained and where there was a limited amount of space for storage.

The major parts of the apparatus consist of a living chamber, a septic tank and an algae tank.

I am now using only the algae *Chlorella* in the apparatus, because to date I have been unable to obtain living cultures of *Scenedesmus* and *Anacystis nidulans*. These types of algae are needed to supplement the necessary amino acids containing sulfur and certain other nutrients in which *Chlorella* is deficient. The algae serve as nourishment for the mice, which I am using as my test animals.

In the septic tank I am using a type of anaerobic bacteria to break down the carbon compounds into methane and then into carbon dioxide and water, and a type to break the urea down to ammonia or some other nitrogen compound that the algae can use.

Operation

Important: Follow the operation through on the Schematic Diagram of the system.

The foul air leaves the living chamber through tube (A) and is pumped by the air pump up through the algae tank, where the carbon dioxide given off by the mice and a few

SCHEMATIC DIAGRAM OF SYSTEM

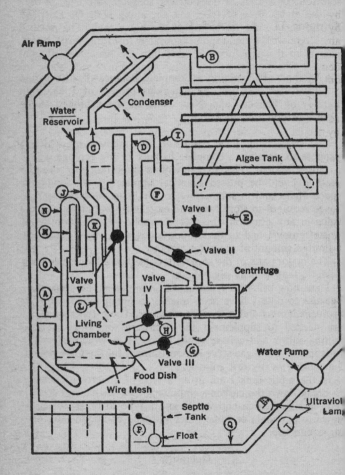

gases from the septic tank dissolve into the nutrient
tion. Dissolved in the nutrient solution, the CO_2 is used
by the algae. Free of CO_2, the air, along with O_2 given off
by the algae, rises to the top of the algae tank. The purified
air, along with water vapor evaporated from the warm water,
passes up through tube (B) and into the water-cooled condenser, where most of the water vapor condenses and runs
out of the condenser into the water reservoir through opening (C). The somewhat drier air also passes out of the condenser into the top of the water reservoir through opening
(C), and then out of the water reservoir through tube (D),
by which it is returned to the living chamber.

The mice will be fed unprocessed algae according to the
following scheme.

When Valve I is in the open position the algae flow
from the algae tank through tube (E) and through Valve I
up into compartment (F) until the surface of the liquid
reaches the end of tube (I), where it will stop rising because
of the air pressure in the top of compartment (F). When
Valve I returns to the closed position and Valve II goes to the
open position, the algae flow out of compartment (F) and
into the centrifuge, which is spun at a high speed until the
algae separate from the nutrient solution and collect around
the outer rim of the centrifuge because they are heavier than
the nutrient solution. Valve III is then opened and the nutrient
solution is drawn off through tube (G), leaving the algae
which, when Valve IV is opened, are drained from the centrifuge and flow through tube (H) into the food dish within
the living chamber. The nutrient solution which was drawn
off in the centrifuge passes down into the septic tank and then
back up into the algae tank.

To supply the mice with a constant drinking water supply,
I have designed the following apparatus. When the water in
the water reservoir reaches a certain level, the water overflows into tube (J), which fills water container (K), which,
after being filled, overflows into tube (L) and runs down
through the living chamber into the septic tank. The water in
container (K) also flows through tube (M), which goes
straight up inside vertical container (N) where it will over-
flow from tube (M) upon demand and run down tube (O),
at the bottom of which it will hang in a drip from which the
mice drink. While not in use the water neither runs freely
out of the tube nor back up the tube.

The excreta of the mice pass through the wire mesh which

acts as the floor of the living chamber into the water be
it, and when the food dish is tipped and Valve V is opene
the water in the water reservoir runs down, washes out the
food dish and continues on down and flushes the pool of
water in the bottom of the living chamber down into the
septic tank. When this occurs, the water at the other end of
the septic tank overflows into compartment (P). When the rising level of the water in compartment (P) reaches a certain
point, the float makes an electrical contact which starts the
water pump and turns on the ultraviolet lamps. The water
pump pumps the water containing dissolved minerals and
organic compounds out of compartment (P), through tube
(Q), between the ultraviolet lamps, which kill most of the
bacteria in the water, and on up through tube (Q) into the
algae tank.

The algae tank is illuminated internally with four white
fluorescent lamps. The fluorescent lamps are inserted into
plastic tubes placed horizontally through the tank. The edges
of the open ends of the tubes are sealed to the edges of
holes in the sides of the tank, thereby permitting easy access
to the fluorescent lamps.

It is my hope that the design of the system presented herein,
with the exception of the design of the algae tank, is an
original contribution to the development of a closed system
adequate to sustain life.

References

1. Gaume, James G., M.D.—"Plants as a Means of Balanc-
   ing a Closed Ecological System"
2. Gaume, James G., M.D.—"Design of an Algal Culture
   Chamber Adaptable to a Space Ship Cabin"
3. Gaume, James G., M.D.—"Sealed Cabins and Artificial
   Atmospheres"
4. Gaume, James G., M.D.-"Nutrition in Space Operations"
5. RIAS, Inc., Report # 29—"Photosynthetic Gas Exchangers," principal investigator: Dr. A. R. Krall and
   authorized contact negotiator: Guy Ullman"

2

"Experimentation in Aerodynamics," the project of Leland
B. Jackson, Atlanta, Georgia, was presented at the Ninth
National Science Fair.

"Introduction

My project is the culmination of four years of experimentation in aerodynamics. In the ninth grade I constructed the wind tunnel as my general science project and used it to determine the lift-drag ratio of several scale model airplanes. In the tenth grade I still worked with lift-drag ratios; but only airfoils, or wings, were experimented with. Various airfoils were classified according to their capabilities and properties and were related to the type aircraft for which they were best suited. (A detailed description of these experiments, along with the graphs and calculations made, may be found in the last section of this log.)

I entered my lift-drag experiments in the 1956 Atlanta Science Congress. In this congress were two projects dealing with photoelastic stress analysis—one in solids and one in liquids. These projects employed polarized light to produce visible patterns of stress in these substances. Since this could be done in solids and in liquids, I wondered if this process might also be employed to show stress in gases, especially around an airfoil. I asked several sources at both Georgia Tech and Lockheed, but could find no evidence that this had ever been tried before. Detailed descriptions of my work with polarized light are included in this log, and although results have so far been negative, many conclusions and projections could be formed.

Still interested in stress analysis, I learned of experiments using a water table which would produce patterns similar to those the polarized light experiments were designed to produce. I therefore designed and constructed a water table and used it to obtain patterns of shock-wave formations and density distributions around an airfoil.

Wind Tunnel Experiments

Having become interested in producing stress patterns in gases through the use of methods employed for photoelastic stress analysis, I mounted polarized glass in both sides of the test section of my tunnel. Photoelastic stress analysis works briefly as follows. A beam of polarized light, or light limited by a piece of polaroid to a vibration in only one direction, is directed through a transparent medium. This medium if unstressed allows the beam to pass unaltered. However, if a stress in the medium has altered the index of refraction in a certain direction, a rotation of the polarized ray will be set up, producing elliptically polarized light. This resulting light, when passed through a second piece of polaroid, produces a pattern of the stress within that medium. These patterns are somewhat circular, alternately colored lines; and the closer these lines are together, the higher the stress is at that point. This rotation from plane to elliptically polarized light is called *birefringence*.

In liquids, if a solution of elongated molecules is at rest, the molecules' random positions will not alter the plane polarized light. However, if the liquid is set in motion, these molecules tend to align themselves with the direction of the flow, and the higher the stress on the liquid, the more they align themselves. This corresponds to the altering of the solid's index of refraction and also produces elliptically polarized light; it is known as *streaming birefringence*.

I was hoping that in gases the difference in the densities surrounding an airfoil in flight would bend the polarized rays so as to produce patterns of the variations around the airfoil (shock waves, density variations, etc.).

Through a new motor, propeller and gear arrangement, I increased the pressure in the tunnel; however, no patterns were produced. I introduced various gases and smokes into the tunnel, including smoke from pine straw, smoldering rags, etc., and carbon dioxide from dry ice in water, but I still was not able to obtain the desired results. I did not continue with experiments along this line, for it was apparent that too great a volume of air passed through my tunnel for an introduced gas or smoke to be anywhere near pure and have any effect. Also, since any introduced gas was not recirculated, it was lost forever once it had passed through the tunnel.

When Mr. Richard T. Whitcomb, head of the supersonic wind tunnel at Langley Air Force Base, Virginia, was in town last year, he observed my project. Although he had never heard of any experiment of this nature, he was of the opinion that my tunnel did not develop enough pressure for an experiment of this type or that air was not dense enough to produce an effect on polarized light.

Although there is the possibility that air molecules are too tenuous and too independent of each other ever to produce an effect upon polarized rays, there are many other approaches using polarized light which still might produce the desired stress patterns. If a smaller, circular, closed wind tunnel system which would recirculate the gas were employed, the gas could obtain a greater velocity through the momentum gathered by recirculation. Also, a gas in an almost pure state could be placed within the system and could be placed under a high pressure even before it was circulated.

If the varying densities around an airfoil do not have an effect on polarized light, it may be that gaseous streaming birefringence can be accomplished if a gas with elongated molecules can be found and employed in the same manner as liquids now are in photoelastic stress analysis.

Water Table Experiments

Still interested in stress analysis, I learned of experiments using a water table which produced patterns similar to those toward which I had been working. My hypothesis on the polarized light experiments had been that if perfected, they would yield a combination of the patterns that could be obtained on a water table. I therefore built a water table in order to produce and study separately the shock-wave and density-distribution patterns.

The water table consists of a tank for the water and a gate at the bottom of this tank which allows a thin, smooth sheet of water to pass over a downwardly sloping piece of glass. A cross section of an airfoil is placed on the glass, and when the flow of water encounters the airfoil, waves are produced in the flow. Under the glass are placed alternately colored lines, and the waves in the flow refract the light rays reflected from these lines, producing patterns of the shock-wave formations. A plain white sheet of paper may be substituted for the lines, in which case the shock waves are shown by the shadows which they cast on this paper.

Patterns of the density distributions around an airfoil also may be produced, for the water displaced by the airfoil on the glass causes the flow to be deeper around the wing. The ratio of this depth to the static or normal depth is equal to the ratio of the densities in the air around a similar airfoil under similar conditions in flight. A chart with points approximately a half inch apart was placed under the glass, and a depth reading was taken at each point. The depth was measured by lowering a pointed object toward the glass until it barely touched the top of the water flow. It was then lowered until it touched the glass, and the number of turns required to do this were carefully counted to the sixteenth of a turn. Since each turn moved the point 1/20 of an inch, the depth could be calculated to 1/320 of an inch. This depth divided by the depth reading taken in the static flow produced the depth ratio, equal to the air density ratio at that point.

A chart showing the pattern of the density distribution around the airfoil was then produced by connecting points of equal ratio to each other by a certain color; the higher the ratio the darker the color used.

The Mach number, or multiple of the speed of sound, which the water table is simulating, is obtained through the following formula: the velocity of the water flow in feet per second divided by the square root of the acceleration of gravity (32.16 ft./sec.^{2}) multiplied by the depth of the water flow in feet. This formula was available for use, but a way to obtain the velocity of the water flow had to be devised.

I knew that pressure is a linear equation with density being constant and depth being the only variable, and therefore the rate of decrease in the pressure of the water in the tank would be even. Therefore, if the time required for the water level to decrease between two depths which were equally above and below the desired depth was clocked, and if the volume of water between these two tank depths was calculated, I would obtain the water velocity at a certain tank depth by dividing this volume by the above described time. The resulting quotient would be a measurement in cubic feet per second. In order for this to be equal to velocity in feet per second, the velocity would have to be multiplied by some measurement in square feet, and this measurement would be the cross-sectional area of the water flow over the table. The velocity of the flow then could be calculated by dividing the volume between the two levels in the water tank by the time required between these two levels multiplied by the cross-sectional area of the flow. This velocity could then be substituted in the Mach number formulas."

Chapter 12 • ZOOLOGY

1

A long-time interest in collecting, identifying and studying the geographic range of mollusks led a Maryland boy, Frank Wayne Grimm of Catonsville, first to sharing his questions and specimens with the curators of the Smithsonian Institution in Washington, D.C., and then to writing a thoroughgoing report on six snails he discovered in the Maryland Piedmont, far from their normal habitat in the mountains of Pennsylvania. He submitted the paper as part of his entry in the Eighteenth Science Talent Search and was not only judged one of the top winners but was awarded the $6000 scholarship because of his outstanding promise as a research scientist. Pictures and maps illustrated the paper, "Unusual Land Snails in Maryland's Susquehanna Valley," a portion of which is quoted here.

"Distribution Records

On March 2, 1958, I collected a small series of snails in the valley of the Susquehanna. In this series were three species which I had found previously in the mountains of Maryland but which I had never seen in the Piedmont. Following this discovery, I became determined to explore the entire length of the valley below the Mason-Dixon line in search of additional records. This search proved quite fruitful, for it revealed the presence of three additional mountain species in the vicinity of the river.

The following compilation includes all of the species in Maryland's Susquehanna Valley which were collected in a period of roughly eight months. In addition to the specific records for the Susquehanna area, I include the over-all range of each species in the United States, plus its occurrence elsewhere in Maryland. I obtained these statewide records over a period of approximately four years, in which I concentrated heavily upon the Piedmont and Appalachian provinces.

Conclusions and Questions Raised

A. A Definite Conclusion Which Raises Several Questions

The preceding data indicate the presence of six snails not heretofore recorded from Maryland's Piedmont: *Triodopsis tridentata, T. notata, Ventridens intertextus, Mesomphix cupreus, Discus patulus* and *Cionella morseana*. Comparison of the ranges of these snails shows both that they are found in the Appalachian Mountains, generally, and that (with the exception of *Cionella morseana*) they range westward through the Ohio-Mississippi drainage region in varying climatic zones. Obviously, they have a wide climatic toleration.

From the data I conclude that the snails must have floated downstream from the Pennsylvania mountains and established themselves in the hills above the river. There they occupy a climatic zone quite warmer than that of the mountains.

After extensive and thorough collecting, I have found none of these species elsewhere east of the Appalachians in Maryland. Since they are distributed widely in the mountains and westward on the Mississippi slope, why are they not found outside the river valley in the Piedmont? Are they blocked by an ecologic barrier which prevents automotive dispersal, or is the Piedmont outside their present peripheries of automotive dispersal?

B. A Tentative Conclusion Which Presents a Challenge

Consideration of the data presented leads me to conclude tentatively that the Piedmont is merely outside their present peripheries of automotive dispersal. This means that the Susquehanna acts as a highway down which the snails can travel rapidly, escaping the time limits set by automotive dispersal. In other words, by means of automotive dispersal the snails may take thousands of years to spread a few miles, whereas by means of adventitious dispersal they may be distributed very quickly. On one hand automotive dispersal is sure to be successful if it does not meet with a barrier. On the other hand, adventitious dispersal, although rapid, does not insure survival. Therefore, the presence of the six snails in Maryland's Piedmont is purely a result of luck. They are there because a chance flood or series of floods have deposited them nearby. Chance determined that they would land safely, and chance determined that they would land in a place which could support them.

In summary, two important facts support the above statements. First, *to my knowledge there are no ecologic or geographic barriers east of the mountains which would prevent the snails from colonizing the Piedmont*. All of these snails are found on the Appalachian Plateau as well as in the true mountains. All are found in the lower southern Appalachians, which have a climate almost identical to that of the northern Piedmont. Second, *already they have begun to colonize the Piedmont by means of adventitious dispersal*.

However, in order to prove my theory conclusively I must find the existing periphery of automotive dispersal for each species. Are any of these snails found elsewhere in the Piedmont, removed from the direct influence of a river or stream?

In the future I hope to answer this question. Meanwhile, I should like to continue exploring the Susquehanna Valley and to expand my field of observation to include the valleys of other major rivers. In this way I may gain a more complete knowledge of the situation elsewhere."

2

William Albert Dunson, of Atlanta, Georgia, was a finalist in the Ninth National Science Fair. His project was called "Radioiodine in Guppies."

"The purpose of this project was to determine iodine distribution in guppies by means of tracer techniques, using radioactive iodine[131]. Through the use of autoradiographs, it was found that the thyroid and the gut of guppies (*Lebistes reticulatus*) definitely concentrated radioiodine. The concentration areas apparently were not affected by the sex of the guppies. The eye pigment and the teeth of the guppies did not concentrate radioiodine, as others have noted in tadpoles. Some guppies were treated prior to their exposure to radioiodine with thiouracil, which reduces the action of the thyroid. Within the time limits of this study, the concentration of radioiodine by the thiouracil-treated guppies was not appreciably different from the normal fish.

This investigation was carried out at the Emory University biology radiolaboratory, under the supervision of an associate professor of zoology. About 53 hours were spent in the laboratory, from July through December, 1957. A total of

69 guppies were taken from an indoor pool in the Emory greenhouse and acclimated in small bowls. Thiouracil (.05%) was placed in the bowls with 23 of these guppies for 1 week. Then 9 normal guppies and 4 thiouracil-treated guppies were exposed to 1 microcurie per milliliter of radioiodine[131] in their bowls for 24 hours. I fixed and embedded 7 of these guppies (4 normal, 3 thiouracil-treated) in paraffin. The guppies were microtomed into 20-micron sections, and 537 selected sections were mounted on 22 slides. The slides were measured for radioactivity with a Beta counter, and then clamped on photographic plates. After 7 days the autoradiographs were developed. The 22 slides were stained, fitted with cover glasses and dried. Photographs were made of the slides of guppy sections with their corresponding autoradiographs. The sections were examined under the microscope, and compared with their autoradiographs. Tables were compiled to show the distribution of radioiodine[131] in these guppies.

This experiment demonstrated that radioiodine[131] is a safe and useful tracer isotope. Autoradiographs are effective in measuring uptake and distribution of radioisotopes. For valid conclusions, zoology research must test large numbers of animals under controlled conditions."

3

"Reproduction and Concentration of Mutations in Guppies" was the project of Ninth National Science Fair finalist Carol McColm, of Farmington, New Mexico.

"Introduction

About fifty-five years have passed since the small viviparous tropical fish, *Lebistes reticulatus*, was first employed for genetic studies. *Lebistes reticulatus*, or "guppy," is well known to all aquarium fanciers. It is characterized by very conspicuous sex differences. The slender male is about 2 cm. long and brightly hued on its lateral surfaces and sometimes on the dorsal and caudal fins. Furthermore, its anal fin is modified into a copulating organ. The female is normally about 4 cm. long and her color is generally an inconspicuous grayish brown.

Although the female normally presents no color pattern, it can transmit its sex-limited genes for color and other traits.

Before the advent of sex hormones, it was almost impossible to differentiate between sex-limited and sex-linked inheritance. With the introduction of these hormones, some of the conclusions of early geneticists must be discarded. To read the early works of Winge and Ditlevsen, one might conclude that only one pair of chromosomes is of much consequence in guppies—the X and Y, but there are twenty-two other pairs to reckon with.

Modifying genes doubtless are present to affect the amount of color shown, the size of spots, the size and shape of fins and the size of the guppy itself. Their number or dominance or recessiveness have not been determined.

The purpose of my experiments was to determine the inheritance of several guppy mutations, some of which have been previously described by some geneticists as sex-linked and located on the Y chromosome. Also, it was to be determined how these mutations could be concentrated, two or three into the same pure line, with four lines in all.

Preliminary Problems Solved

The hormone methyl testosterone (Gordon) can be used to bring out sex-limited color traits in female guppies. Even more effective is pregnenolone (Regnier). The use of .0008 mg. pregnenolone per liter of water will produce an even more intense effect than 1 mg. of methyl testosterone per liter.

Before beginning my study of mutations in guppies, I experimented with guppy environmental factors such as temperature, water quality and food. Guppies proved to be omnivorous, surviving best at 75°-80° F. and at a pH of from 7.1 to 7.5. Acid water produced loss of color and cessation of breeding activity.

Guppies could tolerate a saline water solution of up to one tablespoon sodium chloride per gallon but reproduction was inhibited and the mortality rate increased. This is to be expected, because a sodium chloride solution is known to dissolve the DNA out of the nucleus of the cell by breaking the bonds that link DNA molecules to protein molecules and to one another. Since DNA is the basic hereditary material, it is obvious why reproduction is inhibited by sodium chloride solutions.

In genetic studies, it is imperative that all progeny of the parents be saved and counted to reach an accurate conclusion. Adult guppies, if given the chance, consume their young as soon as they are born. I found two effective solutions to this problem.

Method 1: A fry "trap" based on a mechanical principle can be constructed from a sheet of plastic, bent into a cone and fastened. A small hole is left at the bottom and an "X" of thread sewn over it to prevent the escape of the mother. The cone, placed in a jar of water, houses the mother prior to delivery. The fry, when born, are heavy and sink through the hole to safety.

Method 2: Virgin female guppies can be placed in a tank in which is suspended a small bowl of baby guppies. The females will dash themselves madly against the glass bowl, attempting to get at the baby guppies. But, probably due to unpleasant effects, a conditioned response is induced which causes them to completely ignore baby guppies after from one to three weeks of treatment. This conditioned response remains in effect for the life of the fish. This is the most effective method of preserving guppy offspring from parental cannibalism.

After the guppies are born, the problem of sexing them arises. This must be done before they are sexually mature, to prevent random fertilization. Sexing baby guppies has been considered impossible because of undeveloped sex characteristics at this age. Ordinarily the selective breeder is forced to raise each fish separately, requiring a vast number of containers. This obstacle was overcome by observing that some day-old guppies, when held under a bright light, showed a dark anal spot, while others did not. They were separated and those showing the dark anal spots ultimately developed into females. Sexing based upon this discovery was employed throughout the following experiments.

Materials and Methods

Mutant guppies used in these experiments were obtained from a number of aquarists in Farmington, N. M., as well as from my own aquaria. These mutations consisted of variations in basic body coloring (melanin formation) and tail shape.

An original pedigree system was devised which facilitated identification of each fish with its genotype, parents and offspring.

Ten male mutations for tail shape were isolated with two or more guppies showing the same mutation if possible.

These all were tested for dominance by mating them with females of gold round-tail stock. All males showing mutations for tail shape showed the common gray coloration. All offspring from this mating of gold round tail to gray mutant tail were gray round tail. This proves three important facts about guppy inheritance.

1. The round-tail shape is dominant to all the mutant shapes illustrated below.
2. Gray is dominant to gold body color.
3. Guppies follow the Mendelian Principles of Unit Characters and Dominance.

To ascertain whether guppies would follow the Mendelian Principle of Segregation, I mated each F_1 generation of three of the groups (lyre tail, sword tail & pin tail) brother to sister. The characters segregated as expected according to typical Mendelian inheritance, giving the types and quantities shown below.

The foregoing results proved that guppies also follow the Mendelian Principles of Segregation and Purity of Characters.

Males of the F_2 generation which showed two recessive characters were backcrossed to their gold sisters to determine which carried the sex-limited genes for the mutant tail shapes. The females which proved to carry the sex-limited recessive genes were used to breed pure lines of gold lyre tail, sword tail and pin tail guppies.

With the foregoing information proved about guppy heredity, I planned and conducted matings which concentrated three mutations into one pure line. The types of offspring and quantitites obtained are shown in the accompanying diagram. As before, the backcross was used to separate the desired females.

Summary

1. Inheritance of guppy mutation in these experiments followed the Mendelian Principles of Independent Unit Characters, Dominance and Segregation, Purity of Characters and Random Fertilization.

2. No X or Y linkage was evident in the inheritance of any of the mutations studied in these experiments. Earlier investigators, principally Winge, claimed to find such linkage in their experiments. It is possible that guppy mutations, although similar in appearance, are not always inherited alike. This may account for the differences in inheritance of these mutations.

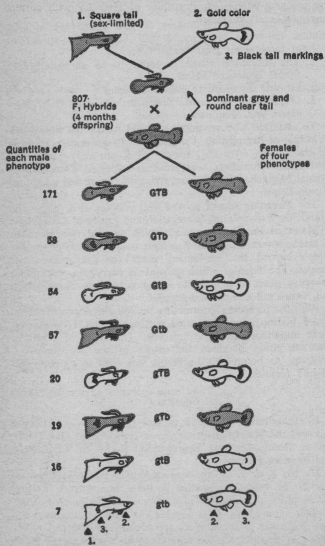

CONCENTRATION OF THREE RECESSIVES

1. Square tail (sex-limited)

2. Gold color

3. Black tail markings

807 F₁ Hybrids (4 months offspring)

×

Dominant gray and round clear tail

Quantities of each male phenotype

Females of four phenotypes

171   GTB

58   GTd

54   GtB

57   Gtb

20   gTB

19   gTd

16   gtB

7   gtb

3.   2.

1.

2.   3.

TOTAL 402

TOTAL 405

3. Mutations for tail shape and basic body color can be concentrated in almost any combination the breeder desires by applying Mendelian Principles of Heredity with correct environmental conditions.

Bibliography

Research Papers:

Regnier, M. T., 1942. "Masculination des Femmelles de *Lebistes Reticulatus* sous l'Influence de la Pregneginolone." *Compt. Rend. Soc. Biol.*, vol. 136, pp. 202-203.

Singe, O., 1922. "One-sided Masculine and Sex-linked Inheritance in *Lebistes Reticulatus*." Genetics, vol. 12, pp. 145-162.

   1923. "Crossing Over between the X and Y Chromosomes in *Lebistes*." *Genetics*, vol. 1, pp. 201-217.

   1927. "The Location of Eighteen Genes in *Lebistes Reticulatus*." *Genetics*, vol. 18, pp. 1-42.

Smith, D. C. and G. M. Everett, 1943. "The Effect of Thyroid Hormones on the Growth Rate, Time of Sexual Differentiation and Oxygen Consumption in the Fish *Lebistes Reticulatus*." *Jour. Exp. Zool.*, vol. 94, pp. 229-240.

Tuchmann, H., 1936. "Action de l'Hypophyse sur la Morphogénese et la Différention Sexuelle de *Girardinus* Guppi." *C. R. Soc. Biol.*, vol. 122, pp. 162-164.

Winge, O. and Eshem Ditlevsen, 1947. "Color Inheritance and Sex Determination in *Lebistes*." *Heredity*, vol. 1, pp. 65-83.

Books:

Abbot, C. G. *Cold-blooded Vertebrates*, Smithsonian Scientific Series, 1934.

Gordon, Myron. *Guppies as Pets*, New Jersey: TFH Publications, Inc, 1955.

Milne & Milne. *The Biotic World and Man*, New York: Prentice-Hall, Inc., 1952.

Srb and Owen. *General Genetics*, California: W. H. Freeman & Company, 1957.

Whitney, Leon F. *All about Guppies*, Connecticut: Practical Science Publishing Company, 1952."

To illustrate the thousands of interesting projects that can be done with great success by even the youngest students in grade school, two sample lists are reproduced here. The first is a list of science fair projects prepared by the Texas Panhandle Science Fair, Amarillo, Texas.

Primary, Grades 1-3, Group Exhibits Only

Physical Sciences

AC Voltage Generation
A Shadow Box to Show Constellations
A Simple Windlass
Chemistry Magic and Test for Nitrogen
Chemistry of Ceramics
Clay Modeling
Flow of Electricity
How Light Is Reflected and Bent
How Much Water Is in the Air?
Phases of the Moon
Rocks of the United States
Steam Turbines
Water Has Energy Because It Has Depth
What You Can See with a Microscope
Evaporation and Rain
How Does the Airport Work?
How Plastics Are Made
How Static Electricity Affects Paper
Importance of Iron and Steel
Simple Machines That Work for Us

Sources of Clothing
Spring Constellations
What Makes an Airplane Move?
The Story of Cotton Processing

Biological Sciences

Conservation of Wild Flowers
Sea Shells
Soil Conservation
Conservation of Wildlife
Ants at Work
How and What Animals Breathe
How Peas Grow
What Foods Have Starch?
Bird Nests
Build Healthy Bodies and Sound Teeth
Collection of Bird Pictures
Regional Wildlife
First Aid Is the Best Aid
How Long Do Animals Live?
How Seeds Travel
Fur Bearers
Parts of Plants We Eat
Plant Germination
Prehistoric Animals
Seed and Plant Study

172

Spiders
Hawks, Useful and Destructive
Growing Leather

Growing Cotton
Growing Rubber
Trees and Their Value to Man

Intermediate, Grades 4-6, Individual or Group Exhibits

Physical Sciences

A Bell System
A Chemical Change
A Crystal Radio Set
Action of a Solenoid
A Door Chime
Air Currents
An Electronic Map of the U.S.
Weaving and Sewing Techniques
A Projector
Measuring the Ocean Depths
Measuring Outer Space
Model Airplanes
Molding
Most Liquids Contain either Acid or Alkali
Operation of a Doorbell •
Parts of an Electric Motor
The Arc Light
A String Pump in Action
A Weather Station
A Cotton Gin
A Wheat Elevator
Cross Section of a Volcano
Cross Section of an Oil Well
Cross Section of the Earth
Distillation of Water
Power and Food from the Sea
An Electromagnet
Expansion and Contraction of Liquids
History in Shells
Types of Fuel
Heat Can Produce Electricity

Fire Must Have Air to Burn
How Electricity Is Made
An Electromagnetic Crane
Machines and Tools
Parts of a Sailboat
Parts of a Windmill
Polar Constellations
Principles of a Transformer
Products Made and Mined in Texas
Products of Oil
Jet Propulsion, Natural and Man-made
The Quartz Family
A Reed Basket
Resources of the U.S.
Rotation of Planets
Sending Messages by Electric Light
Snowflakes
Space Travel Is Coming
Space Problems in Gravity
Steam Propulsion
Steam Turbines
The Fulcrum and the Lever
The Planets
The Seasons
Water Is a Compound of Hydrogen and Oxygen
Working Principles of a Gasoline Engine
Workings of a Telegraph
Workings of a Television Camera
Workings of an Irrigation Pump
Air Pressure in a Mercury Barometer

Alaska, Its Size and Re-
  sources
Astronomy
Birth of a Balloon
The Blinker Light
Causes of the Seasons
Bulbs in Series and Parallel
The Climate of Your Home
Chemurgy
Chlorophyll
Climate
Electric Eye
Electromagnetism
Fluorescent Lights
Functions of a Camera
Glass and Its Uses
How to Develop a Picture
How Traffic Signals Work
Inside a Cave
Machines Make Work Easier
Man's Natural Resources
Manufacturing Machinery
Mercury
Minerals: Origin, Distribu-
  tion and Uses
Our Community Planning
Our Solar System
Phases of the Moon
Printing and Its Value to
  Man
Salt and Its Uses
Shells of the World
Simple Machines
Sound
Sulfur
Fingerprinting
The Telegraph Key
Which Metals Conduct Heat?
The Telephone
Train Signals
Water Finds Its Own Level
Water   Supports   Heavy
  Weights
Weather and Man

Biological Sciences

A Cow's Horns
A Model Arm
Butterflies
Growing Trees
Human Eye
Inside Fruit
Leaf Characteristics
Fruits of the Texas Panhan-
  dle
Migration of Birds
Nutrition
Parts of a Bird
Parts of a Flower
Parts of a Hen's Egg
Parts of a Horse
Plants Grow Toward Light
Prehistoric Animals
Seed Collection
State Flowers and Birds
Swat that Fly
Rats Are Eating Your Food
The Beaver
The Coyote
The Jack Rabbit
The Prairie Chicken
Tales, Trails and Tails of the
  Wolf
The Earthworm, Master Plow-
  man
The Human Heart
The Life Story of a Tree
Carbon Dioxide and Man
The Way to Test for Food
  Starch
A Garden
A Healthy Breakfast
A Balanced Aquarium
Bees
Bird Album
Care and Feeding of Birds
Cotton Culture
Ecology   of   Our   School
  Grounds

Food Values
Fat Is Fatal
Habitat Studies
How a Tooth Decays
How Plants Reproduce
Insects: Bad Guys or Good Guys?

Mammals of Texas
Parts of the Eye
Primitive Animals
The Age of Reptiles
The Solar System
Our Friend the Wren
Wild Flowers of Texas

Junior, Grades 7-9, Individual or Group Exhibits

Physical Sciences

A Homemade Cloud Chamber
A Homemade Cotton Gin
A Homemade Flour Mill
A Look into the Future
An Amplifying Unit
A Nuclear Reactor
Astronomy vs. Atoms
Building a Bird House
Building a Bridge
Building Dams
Change in Boiling Points with Altitude
Construction of a Pipeline
Crude Weather Barometer
Crystal Radio Set
Decomposition of Water by Electric Current
Different Kinds of Cloth
Drilling an Oil Well
Early Methods of Drilling
Earth's Crust
Climate Makes Civilizations
Electricity
Exploring the Universe
Exploring the Arctic
Facts and Preparation of Oxygen
Foucault's Pendulum
Forms in Geometry
Formations in the Earth
Formations for Petroleum
Four-Pole Motor

History of Architecture
History of Archaeology
History in Rocks
How to Build a House
How to "Soup" an Engine
Homemade Photoelectric Cell
How a Steam Engine Works
How a Fire Engine Works
How Fires Start
How Lakes are Formed
How the Water Table Rises and Lowers
Mathematical Operations with a Wheatstone Bridge
Mathematical Philosophy
Meteor Craters in West Texas
Midget Transmitter
Mineral Collection
Miniature Zinc Mine
Miniature Helium Plant
Miniature Refinery
Model of a Periscope
Observatory
Oil from the Ground to You
Operating a Refinery
Opaque Projector
Petroleum Production
Petroleum Is Where You Find It
Products Made from Petroleum
Products Made from Natural Gas
Radio, AM, FM and Stereo
Removing Stains

Relation of the Sun to the Earth

Rubber: Synthetic and Natural

Safe Plumbing

Sensitive Air Thermometer

Stars as We See Them

Star or Planet?

Stratosphere

Sulfuric Acid

Tempera Painting

Types of Printing

Types and Styles of Lettering

Testing Conductivity

Testing for T.B.

The Hydraulic Brake

Drum or Disk Brakes?

Turbines in Our Autos?

The Parts of a Volcano

The Pendulum

The Weapons of War

The Rocket: Its Uses

The Principles of an Electric Refrigerator

The Principles of a Gas Refrigerator

The Heat Pump

The Solar Family

How to Take a Fingerprint

Insulation Keeps Heat Where You Want It

Internal Combustion Engines

Increasing Horsepower

Minerals of West Texas

Lines of Magnetic Force

Transformers

Tricks Our Eyes Play On Us

Atoms

Certain Chemicals Give Off Colored Light When Burned

Code-sending Oscillator

Controlling Heat

Crude Oil By-Products

Effects of Atomic Blasts

Fire Extinguisher

Hydrogen Gas

Helium Gas

Ink

Lakes of West Texas

Length of Light Waves

Magnetic Door

Magnetic Motor

Magic Doors

Mechanics of Magic

Method of Securing Water by Wind Power

Method of Taking Energy from Sunlight

Microwaves

Miniature Gasoline Engine

How Deep Can a Well Be?

The Coaxial Cable

Mirror Grinding for Telescopes

Model of a Geyser

North American Ice Ages

One-Tube Portable Radio

Operating the DEW Line

Ores and Minerals of Texas

Our Trembling Earth

Principles of an Electric Doorbell

Push-Button Living

Rayon, Orlon, Nylon

Science in Entertainment

Securing a Water Supply

Sources and Use of Light

Surface of the Moon

Tests for Kinds of Cloth

The Moon

The Principle of Jet Propulsion

UFO (Unidentified Flying Objects)

Propulsion: Jet or Rocket?

Thermal Efficiency of Insulated Bags

Relative Humidity: What It Means to You

The Role of Cosmetics

Making Cosmetics

The Light Spectrum

Story of Oil

Unusual Batteries

The Transistor, Mighty Mouse

Uses of Electricity in the Home

Water Purification

What Nature Can Do with Dripping Water

Model Electric Motorcar

Models of Rocket Ships

Model of the Canadian River Dam

Model of the Expressway

Modern Television Station

An Arc Furnace

Superheterodyne Radio

Every Man is Superman on the Moon

Stereophonic Sound

Aviation Hazards and Safety Devices

The Snark

The Sidewinder Rocket

The Nautilus Atomic Submarine

The Sound Barrier

Sonic Boom

Code Sending

Model of a Navy Cruiser

Model of an Airport

Design for Downtown

Design for a Shopping Center

Model of a Waterwheel

Black Light

Bridges

How Canal Locks Work

Comparing Old and New Telephones

Dam and Power Plant

Electric Elevator

Electronics: What Is It?

How a Distributor Works

How a Diesel Engine Works

How Acid Is Used in Oil Wells

How Casing Is Set in Oil Wells

Model Power Plant

Model Spaceship

Newton's Third Law of Motion

Operation of a Turbine

Turbine Engines for Automobiles

Traffic Control with a Cloverleaf

Progress in Road Construction

Radio-controlled Aircraft

The Gear Pump

Processing Wood for Use

Canadian River Dam Distribution System for Water

Clay Model of Indian Dwellings

Development of the Automobile

Engineering in Everyday Life

Four-Cycle Engines

Two-Cycle Engines

Free-Piston Engines

Gravity Water Distribution

Heights Above Sea Level

How Hydroelectric Power is Made

Model of the Earth's Interior

Model of Road Intersections

Model Contour Plowing

Radio Construction

Simple Appliance Wiring

Safe Home Wiring

Story of Steel

Story of Aluminum

Television

Strokes of a Gasoline Engine
The Water Table
A Three-Stage Rocket
Types of Automobile Transmissions
Various Methods of Communications
Working Parts of a Drilling Rig
Designs for Autos of the Future

Biological Sciences

Inside the Human Tooth
Our Gift of Life: Blood
Cancer
Glands in the Body
The Body's Emergency System
The Thumb, Man's Greatest Weapon
Prehistoric People
Safety in the Home
Saving the Soil with Plowing
Safety on the Job
Animal and Human Blood
Animals in Your Everyday Life
Flower Models in Paper
Flowers on Stamps
Animals on Stamps
The Pharmacist and the Physician
Compounding Medicines
Flowers in Plastic
Flowers in Wax
A Study of Leaf Growth
Bacterial Indicator
Beehives
A Bat's Life
African Violets
Age of Dinosaurs
American Plants of Medical Value
Amoeba

Anatomy of the Head
Anatomy of the Heart, Mammalian
Animal IQ
Animal Psychology
Ant House
Better Farming through Science
Bird Identification
Birds of West Texas
Camouflage for Animals
Cause and Control of Pasture Fires
Effects of Vitamin B Deficiency
Circulation of the Blood
Conservation of Soil and Water
Cotton Production
Cross Sections of Stems
Uses for Wheat Straw
Dairy Industry in West Texas
Development and Growth of Lima Beans
The Soybean
Sesame Seed Culture
The Story of the Horse
Diet to Lose Weight
Animals in Embryo
Soap from Yucca
Parasites in Cattle
The Food Structure
Grafting Methods
Effects of Sweet, Sour and Neutral Soil
Histology Slides of Animal Tissue
History of a Tree
Homemade Soap
Termites in Your Timbers
I Am Studying Taxidermy
Inside the Earth (worm)
Irrigation Project
Locating Water Wells
Leaf Structure

Life and Death
Life in the Pasture Pond
Plant Propagation
Regeneration
Breeding for Beef
Breeding for Milk
Breeding for a New Strain
By-Products of Corn
Amazing Maize
Skeletons
Cereal Grains
The Heart of the Wheat Kernel
Stomach and Liver
The Canary
The Digestive System
The Eye
The Human Brain
The Lung of a Human vs. The Lung of a Pig
The Spices of Life
Taste, Bud?
Structure of the Human Ear
The World We Live In, by Mr. and Mrs. Red Ant
Tobacco
Wardian Jar
Water and Its Work
Woods: To Burn, Build and Burnish
Animal Parasites
Balanced Aquarium
Bird Identification Chart
Native Grasses of West Texas
The Human Foot

Callouses, Corns and Complaints
Past and Present Man
Products of Native Woods
Bone Structure of a Cat
Care of the Hands
Cotton and Its Uses
Cross Section of a Flower
Effects of Nutrition on White Mice
Everything but the Squeal
Fossils
How and Why We Save Wildlife
The Human Ear
The Growing Seasons of West Texas
Metamorphosis of a Butterfly
Mosquitoes
Multipurpose Farm Ponds
Seven Stages in Development of Man
Shelters through the Ages
Snakes Alive
Study of Protozoans
Teeth of the Human Mouth
The Care, Feeding and Breeding of Dogs
The Cat Family
The Wasp, Master Papermaker
Vegetable Vitamins
Wild Ducks and How to Encourage Them

Another example of what pre-high school students can do is revealed in the science fair catalog of University Park School, University Park, Maryland.

The Universe

Sun, Earth and Moon
Our Changing Earth

The Elliptic (Earth's Orbit)
The Solar System
Members of the Universe
The Earth Beneath Us

AT least part of the reason people are drawn to careers in science is the now nearly unique opportunity to explore unmapped territory where anything may happen.

Apparently the human spirit, especially the young human spirit, harbors a great longing to venture into mystery, to struggle with it and to emerge with sketch maps and a pocketful of samples.

A special light glows in a scientist's face when you ask him to suggest expeditions into areas of the unknown that have been glimpsed, flagged by pioneers or deduced by someone with an especially far-reaching mind.

He may, for example, propose the question of how physics, mathematics, biophysics and, perhaps, biochemistry can be brought together to explain the mysteriously orderly processes that develop, maintain and reproduce living matter.

Or he may suggest investigating the possibility that a unified theory of liquids can be evolved through research in liquid state physics and the use of electronic computers.

Or: What size city and what population density will insure human "quality" and the privacy that seems essential to creativity?

How is the delicate balance of growth and death of tissue cells maintained? How is the necessary death of cells brought about at precisely the "right" time?

What guides migrating birds? Do they respond to polarized light, as bees and ants do? If not, to what do they respond?

Is there a relationship between exceptional human perceptions and the radar of bats, the homing instinct of pigeons?

How does "reinforced learning," the new education method, teach so rapidly?

Why are trees round in form rather than square? Is there any significance in the thickness of the leaves of plants?

What will happen tomorrow—or in the next generation—in physical, geometrical and electron optics; in photometry; in the measurement of physical, magnetic and other properties of solid state thin films; in the fields of digital memories and logic, transistor circuitry, magnetics, microminiaturization of circuits and components, electrical wave filters, information theory?

Student-scientists still in high school are unwilling to wait for a distant day and a Ph.D. degree to begin exploring such exciting questions. Many want very much to join the search immediately, and some of them have.

Given a moderate amount of professional guidance, it should be possible for you, too, to learn enough background facts to scout out at least a small corner of new territory.

Whether or not you actually make any discoveries is relatively unimportant, say senior scientists. Much more important is that indescribable thrill of finding truth for yourself. And once you experience that, it is not likely that you will ever forget it.

The following collection of interesting questions, inventions, discoveries and suggestions has been assembled to stimulate your imagination or pique your curiosity enough to start the wheels grinding. A great many of these are drawn from reports of current work discussed in newspapers and science publications such as *Science News Letter, Science, Scientific American*, etc. Other ideas can be found in *Thousands of Science Projects*, published by Science Service, which lists the winning projects from the Science Talent Searches, National Science Fairs and affiliated science fairs. Still other ideas can be found in the publications listed in the final chapter of this book.

Aeronautics and Space Sciences

A man-made "nose," more powerful than the human nose, is needed for sensing danger odors in military aircraft. Odor-detecting agents of the past, when used in experiments, have proved toxic to crews.

An automatic aileron trim control has been developed for keeping small private planes on course in bad weather.

A navigational "brain" has been devised to help control the flight of high-speed planes through intricate flight patterns.

A navigational push button that remembers the way home has been developed.

Progress continues on production of a chemical-fuel-burning bomber designed to reach 2200 miles per hour and altitudes of nearly 100,000 feet and to make round-trip transcontinental runs without refueling.

A new paint with only a small chance of detection by radar has been developed.

A midget low-cost wind tunnel has been built to determine air flow up to three times the speed of sound.

How is the FAA planning to conduct its survey of jet fatigue effects on crews?

Ion propulsion, electrostatic acceleration of charged particles of colloid size and plasma acceleration are among the forms of propulsion devices being developed for space vehicles. These devices, along with containment (in the hope of controlling the energy of nuclear fusion) and flow modification, form the three fields of magnetofluidmechanics, the new science which will undoubtedly have practical applications soon.

Some important problems in aeronautics include: converting heat directly into electricity; getting more power per pound of fuel; propulsion in space-plasma jets, ion and photon rockets; finding lightweight, long-duration systems to provide electrical power in space without nuclear radiation; finding ways to protect man against radiation in space; study of cosmic rays; study of properties of intermediate isotopes for use in lightweight shielding.

Theories concerning the gravity fields of stars may provide new understanding of the nature of atomic nuclei.

Application of quantum-mechanics concepts to real chemical systems may help explain the internal structure and properties of materials.

What are some of the methods in use for air traffic control? Can you design new ones?

What are some of the fuels in use for jets today? What new ones are in the experimental stage?

What qualities are looked for in basic materials needed for construction of nuclear propulsion systems, space vehicles, missiles, rocket motors, naval vessels and electronic devices?

Why is the Army's new Flying Duck of importance?

Why is it so difficult to detect, ahead of explosion, any bombs planted aboard commercial aircraft? Can you devise a method of detection?

What effect does weightlessness have on algae?

Investigate the details and significance of the experiment known as the Moon Garden.

What is the purpose of a radioactive-cobalt chamber?

What is the gas cushion technique for safely landing instruments on the lunar surface?

What are the principles and uses of the Mighty Mouse?

How does a liquid propellant rocket differ from a solid propellant rocket? What are the advantages of each? What future developments can you predict?

What are some of the proposed and already employed uses of rockets? What other uses might be developed?

What are some of the disadvantages of chemical rockets? Can these be overcome?

What is being done internationally about space laws dealing with frequencies for space transmissions?

What is the purpose of a space helmet? Can you suggest improved designs of such space equipment?

Archaeology

Discuss the social life and customs of the Brazilian Indians known as the Botocudos.

Explore the difference in meaning of the words *archaeology* and *anthropology*.

Investigate two new dating methods for determining the age of objects: recording the electron glow of dishes and pottery when heated; measuring moisture layers in objects made of volcanic glass.

What is known of the primitive tree-dwelling people who now inhabit only the Indian Archipelago and parts of Malaysia?

Why was the finding of the tomb of Tutankhamen, an Egyptian king, of such great importance?

What were some of the important archaeological discoveries made in the first half of the nineteenth century?

Astronomy

Where is the largest solar telescope located in the U.S.? How large is its mirror?

What are the chief colors shown among stars and what do they indicate?

What are meteorites and some of the theories of their origin?

What are tektites?

How much is known about the comet Burnham, dicovered December 30, 1959?

What is the scientific origin of the ancient belief of seeing blood on the moon?

What is the ionosphere and what practical purposes has it served?

Are asteroids produced by the disruption of an old planet that formerly moved around the sun between the orbits of

Mars and Jupiter? Or are they formed from debris left over when main planets came into being?

Biological Sciences

General

What are the chemical "time clocks" of cells?

Studies of the action of lithosperm by means of extracts from a dried preparation of the plant show a decided effect on the secretion of sex hormones in animals. No research has yet been done in human biology.

At Louisiana State University a two-year research program has been financed for search of microbes that will refine oil. It is believed that just as the human body acts as a catalyst to change the chemical structure of foods, microorganisms should exist that can change hydrocarbon-like structures to purify petroleum fractions.

Present knowledge of the universe indicates that some form of life exists outside the earth, very likely on Mars. Biologists are urged to design equipment and develop systems that will automatically make comparisons of life on earth with that on other planets, even if man should not be present to make the tests.

What tests do scientists make for cellulose to determine whether a tiny living thing is plant or animal?

Will the study of slime molds yield clues to the formation of various kinds of cells and the process of cell differentiation in plants and animals?

What is the importance of photosynthesis to the balanced aquarium?

Botany

What causes leaves of deciduous trees to change color and drop off?

Study the effects of the compaction of soil on plants.

Investigate the effect of gibberellin on conifers. Studies indicate very little effect, possibly because of an internal surplus of the compound or true indifference to it. Additional work that needs to be done includes:

1. Determining the effects of gibberellin on inherently small conifers such as the MacNab cypress, bristle cone pine, one-seed juniper, Canadian yew.
2. Testing the effect of gibberellin on long leaf pine during its early dwarf (grass) stage.

An experiment with spinach leaves and vitamin K shows that this vitamin may play the role of a "neutral corner" for hydrogen atoms separated from water. This study provides another step in the understanding of photosynthesis.

That ethyl alcohol stimulates growth in algae and seedlings has already been reported by researchers. Further studies are being made about the use of alcohol that has accumulated under airless or anaerobic conditions, and what takes place in the plant that makes such alcohol possible in air.

Do botanists hold the key to solving the problem of feeding the world's constantly increasing population? The use of foods like seaweed and algae has not proved sufficient to solve this problem. Botanical research is needed to increase agricultural productivity along the lines of breeding and selecting better plants and improved plant nutrition and protection.

The U. S. Government needs someone to devise an economical method for harvesting algae. For use as animal fodder, fertilizer and food for human consumption, these plants would have to be gathered out of water and concentrated, which is an expensive process.

The rate of plant growth may be controlled in the future by filtering sunlight, according to the experiments of two scientists on the one-celled plant, chlorella. Other scientists are studying plants growing under red and blue artificial light and the afterglow resulting from radiation by these lights used separately or together.

Investigate the curious world of plant galls, such as the goldenrod bunch gall, the willow pine cone gall, the flower gall on ash trees, spruce cone gall on Norway spruce, the poplar vagabond gall, black knot on plum and cherry trees, the oak hedgehog gall, the spiny witch hazel gall.

Will there soon be lawns that need no mowing and dwarf trees that yield normal-sized fruit? Gibberellin has been proved to promote plant growth, and research is under way for discovery of an antigibberellin to suppress growth without affecting the yield of normal crops.

Can sick plants, like animals, be treated with "pills" to combat disease caused by fungi? Antibiotics, fungicides, growth and antigrowth compounds are being studied with the hope of introducing substances into plants that will cure diseases already existent—an improvement over preventive sprays and treatments now used before a disease develops.

Three plant-growth regulating compounds have been tested and found movable throughout the plant and exuded from plant roots. Research is now being conducted with hope that a chemical to protect plants against diseases, insects or nematodes will be discovered that will also prove mobile within plants.

By the use of ordinary hypodermic syringes, scientists have injected radioactive carbon, C-14, into two-year-old pine trees for one of the first controlled studies of cellulose growth in living trees. While the research is still in its preliminary stages, first results indicate a strong possibility for higher yields of cellulose per tree, plus improved quality from these "hot" trees. If this proves to be the case, the tire and cellophane industries may be helped toward greater production, efficiency and lowered costs.

Experiments are being carried out for further proof that certain chemicals, such as riboflavin, adenine and gibberellic acid produce heat resistance in plants. Further research may enable food crops to be grown in desert areas and increase yields in cultivated areas already existing.

An Indian scientist reported at the Ninth International Botanical Congress on a thirty-day experiment with native climbing plants that had been subjected to recorded flute music. Height, average number of leaves, length and breadth of leaves and number of roots showed increases of twenty-five to fifty percent over growth of plants in a control group. A student at a Kansas City junior high school, trying a similar growth experiment with jazz, Dixieland, classical, and sound-effects recordings, discovered that plants responded best to the sound-effects record.

Why should peas planted directly in moist soil produce a higher percentage of healthy plants than pea seedlings soaked in water prior to planting?

Plants, when injected with human red blood cells, have reacted like people, producing serum containing antibodies. Such is the report of a Yugoslav medical researcher. If true, one practical application might be the use of this serum as a typing serum for testing human blood.

It has recently been discovered that turbulence, or rapid and irregular movement of the air or water, is probably responsible for higher photosynthetic rates in nature. Experiments with bottled water plants and similar plants growing in a channel under natural conditions have proved that the latter plants showed twice as much photosynthetic activity.

The genes of corn plants have been found to break the

old genetic laws. Recent experiments show that the red color in the husks, stems and other parts of corn plants is controlled by the "converter" gene and the partner gene it affects, so that only weak red color appears in successive generations. The gene for intense red is permanently converted to weak red.

Both Western and Russian scientists are working on the inheritance of environmental effects on plants. A Russian botanist has soaked the seeds of several kinds of plants in water, dried them and produced plants with considerable drought resistance. His claim that several successive generations remain drought resistant was not supported with evidence.

An antiseptic varnish, containing 0.25% phenyl mercury nitrate, may soon be available for combatting fungus growth in trees. Experiments showed that the varnish alone, or when combined with several common fungicides, was not sufficient.

A "vaccine" is being sought that will prove toxic to the parasitic dwarf mistletoe, but not to the ponderosa pine on which it grows. Effects of research are being tested by atomic energy tools, including radioautographs.

The initial acceleration of a dwarf mistletoe seed shot out of its pod is thousands of times faster than that of a man-made rocket.

The aster yellow virus, which affects asters, lettuce, spinach and carrots, is carried from sick to healthy plants by the corn leafhopper. This insect, when it sucks up the virus, is able to eat and thrive on foods that normally would have poisoned it—asters and carrots. A new field of research into the possible beneficial effects of plant viruses may therefore open up.

The growing world population and present wear and tear on farm land probably make it necessary to develop tropical areas into major producers of food. Many plants suitable for farming in temperate zones are not suitable for the rainy tropics, because the natural vegetation of the tropics is so different. While fertilizers are being used, important substances, such as phosphorus and potassium, are in short supply and make indefinite experimentation in the tropics difficult.

Experiments with a "mechanical cow" that extracts fifty percent of the protein from leaves or grass are being made by the British Agricultural Research Council, with the idea of combatting malnutrition in undeveloped countries. After filtering, the protein is separated from the juice thus obtained. Juiceless choppings and waste juice are being fed to pigs, and in small-scale experiments they are thriving on the new diet.

Experiments have shown that some unknown globulins in skim milk halt the destructive effects of a plant virus in tobacco, pepper and tomato plants. Further research may show that this milk substance will be useful in controlling animal virus diseases.

Derived seaweed products, chiefly colloids, already have much use as thickeners and agents in a variety of manufactures, such as icings, chocolate and cosmetic creams. The demand for natural products of seaweed is growing rapidly for animal foods and fertilizers. Experiments with kelp meal, manufactured only in Norway, are still going on in this country because of the high protein, vitamin and mineral content of this meal.

Entomology

Why is it necessary to establish a program for eradication of the imported fire ant? Studies are being conducted at the Harvard University Biological Laboratories on the odor trail produced by this ant. The nature of the odor trail and the way it is laid down need to be studied.

Is the foreign fly, *Musca autumnalis*, to become as much of a menace to cattle as the Japanese beetle has proved to gardeners and farmers? A United States Department of Agriculture researcher reports that the fly, first reported in Long Island, New York, in 1953, has become so widespread a pest that it is impractical to attempt any eradication program. However, entomologists all over the country are alert to its danger.

The use of modern organic insecticides against the boll weevil, boll worm and cotton flea hopper is making possible the production of forty-two percent more cotton every year.

Recent investigations show that DDT, the effective insecticide, hates water. It concentrates on the upper water surface very rapidly and clings to walls and bottoms of containers of various materials, so that within twenty-four hours more than half the DDT evaporates. Studies are in progress to see whether changes in application methods may lead to more effective results.

Experiments have shown that heat from radio-frequency electric fields kills in seconds the insects destructive to stored wheat and wheat shorts, without damaging the wheat. Agricultural scientists are working to make the radio-frequency method commercially practical.

Zoology

What are the differences between centipedes and millipedes as to structure and life habits?

What causes the schooling behavior of fish?

Study six species of birds, formerly common in the United States, that have become nearly extinct. Study six mammals that are likewise endangered.

What are the chief North American flyways?

Because of the nine nerve cells which spiny lobster hearts contain, experiments with them may illustrate the effect that certain drugs could have on human nerve cells. A clue to the release mechanisms of certain hormones in man might also be furnished through a simultaneous study of the lobster's pericardial organ.

Hundreds of recordings of bird songs, chiefly those of song sparrows, indicate that heredity is the basis for many features of songs, but that birds also imitate other birds' songs and thus add to their repertoire.

Salt scattered on highways in the winter has been known to cause a strange malady, when eaten, which has led to the death of rabbits and some birds. The malady was traced to its source and the same symptoms have been induced in laboratory experiments.

The "wise old owl" is rather a dumb bird as birds go; crows have been known to exhibit more seeming intelligence and are credited with high IQ's. Yet what looks like intelligent action may possibly be blind luck, as in the case of English birds that opened the caps of milk bottles to take their morning sip of milk. It would be interesting to find out if one bird mastered the trick and then taught it to another.

Two scientists of the British Museum of Natural History, London, report on seasonal studies of the skull of the common shrew which indicate that the brain case depths increase from January to July and decrease for the rest of the year.

Greater variations are found with shrews living in colder winter temperatures. Similar studies of shrews from different parts of North America would prove of interest, according to these scientists.

Luciferin, a light-emitting compound found in fireflies and other creatures that glow in the dark, has recently been removed from a fish. Now that relationships have been established between the luminescent systems of different organisms, studies of the effects of drugs, heat and cold, and antibiotics on organisms will be possible with the use of extracts of luminescence.

Experiments on a captured whippoorwill show that air temperatures from 35.6° F. to 66° produce torpor, during which state body and air temperatures are relatively the same. When both temperatures were raised to about 59° F., the bird awoke. Shivering, increased respiration, a rise in body temperature to a normal of about 100°, and a rise in oxygen consumption were then observed. Scientists are interested in the processes of hibernation and related "slowdowns," because they provide new information on the metabolism of living organisms.

It has been reported that the amount of wave action, even when there is no change in the salt content of the water, affects fauna along the coast. In sheltered spots and in calm waters the fauna are far more rich and varied.

Can the three ways in which birds scratch their heads (direct; indirect, with leg over draped wing; and perch scratching) be used as a means of classification? What is the biological function and motivation of head scratching in birds?

How does the dolphin get a free ride swimming near a ship's bow? How can the dolphin swim several times faster than predicted from drag and muscle power?

Chemistry

How do catalysts work?

+ Investigate soluble compounds that are in use for secret writing.

+ Study substances found in water which may make it dangerous for drinking purposes.

Investigate chemistry in relation to the behavior of viruses. Viruses usually breed true, but occasionally a new strain appears and becomes dangerous. How can this be combatted?

The U. S. Department of Agriculture has developed a

new chemical treatment for cotton, based on use of water soluble acid colloid of methylolmelamine. This forms resin which penetrates the outer portion of the fiber cell and renders the material more resistant to rot and weather. The treatment, as proved by other research, can be used with some fabric coloring pigments to increase cotton's resistance to sunshine.

Experiments with catalysts of an organometallic sort, mainly combinations of aluminum, carbon and hydrogen containing compounds, and titanium and chlorine, are being conducted, chiefly in Germany and Italy These new catalysts may make possible increased mileage for tires, prevention of automobile engine knocks and a variety of other chemical reactions.

Radiation chemistry experiments are being undertaken to show what useful by-product material may be produced. The plastics field is one in which there is already promise of success.

Experiment with making natural dyes from items like onion skins, crab apple bark, sassafras roots, wild clover, blueberries, wild plum roots, broom sedge, red maple bark, spinach, beets and yucca roots.

Experiment with perfumes made from spices, flavorings and other ordinary household ingredients.

A foaming additive for concrete mixes has been developed from fish scales mixed with special chemicals, adding polyglycols for stability. It can be pumped vertically and horizontally; it repels moisture, insulates well, is fast drying.

Investigate ways of breaking down gases from automobile exhausts, reducing smog and the effects of exhaust fumes on human beings.

Study and explain the rainbow of colors seen in the soap bubbles in the dishpan or laundry tub. What interesting questions occur to you concerning the behavior of bubbles?

Investigate applications of colloid chemistry in the fields of catalysis, pigments and soils.

Nuclear magnetic resonance makes possible a greater knowledge of the more complex forms of phosphorus. Research on new phosphorus compounds is being undertaken in commercial laboratories and may result in greater use of such compounds.

Basic research in the chemistry and metallurgy of materials at high temperatures is much needed.

What causes decay in paper and what is being done about it?

Engineering and Technology

Devise a simple and inexpensive method of measuring radioactivity of milk and other food products.

Study five materials which are used for the making of paper.

Explain the process known in tannery wet-work as bating and show why it is necessary.

What are the advantages of stainless steel for tanker construction? What other materials or types of construction might prove practical?

Flexible plastic strips containing a magnetized metallic powder are being utilized to insulate refrigerator doors and to keep them shut. Possibilities for other commercial uses of these magnets seem almost unlimited.

A push-button type combination microscope and camera has already seen practical use in the field of medical research for studying cancer cells, and in geology for studying fine details of earth formations and fossils. Are there other fields in which this instrument may do practical service?

"Saw kerf chips" are a modified type of sawdust produced by a new saw blade with less teeth and a larger bite. This new type of sawdust has already been used successfully in manufacturing pulp and paper, but tests are being made for wider application of the process.

The first organic solar battery has been developed at the University of California. Such batteries may, in the future, prove important in space flight, for satellites and for specialized uses on earth, but their development is still at an early experimental stage.

Besides the Reynolds Aluminum submarine, designed at the Southwest Research Institute, San Antonio, Texas, scientists there are attempting to develop design concepts for the deep-diving submarine of the future. The best geometric shapes, materials and combinations of materials are being sought to enable a submarine to withstand intense pressures encountered at great depths while still allowing it to remain buoyant.

A revolutionary new scheme for transmitting intelligence is wanted which is not dependent on any method used today, such as electrical impulses, electromagnetic waves or sound waves. The messages sent out must be detectable only by the desired receiver and impossible for an enemy to intercept.

The government wants a means for erasing from fields of snow all telltale signs that any object, from a staff car to a whole army, has passed. Enemy photorecon planes can detect recent disturbances in a field of snow by comparing photographs.

The Army wants a cheap additive which will transform surface soil into hard pavement. It would be used to solidify byroads, bridge approaches, sandy beaches and missile launching sites, where rocket blasts cause temporary dust storms. This discovery must be easy to mix and apply to wet or dry soils without complicated, heavy equipment. Also, another branch of the Army wants an invention to soften hard ground.

The government urgently needs: a silencer for rocket propulsion; a nonmagnetic hand compass; a universal light-aircraft landing gear, good for land, water and snow; an aspirin-size pill usable as fuel for a long haul.

The armed services want a device for spotting mines from airplanes. The detector should be responsive to the explosive itself and not solely to metals, since mines have also been encased in plastic, wood and other materials.

Enumerate some of the advantages of multifuel diesel engines.

Why is it necessary to make the pistons in the front wheel cylinders of an automobile larger than those in the rear wheels?

A new device for testing fibers is the ballistic test. How does it work and what is its purpose?

In what fields of industry have rare earth alloys proved useful? What other uses might be developed? Explore the use of radioisotopes in manufacturing processes.

How might internal air conditioning and illumination be affected by the new air wall construction?

Dielectric heating is a new method of using high voltage through nonconductive surfaces to produce heat. This new use of high voltage is fast but too costly for commercial use as yet.

Research has been undertaken on the production of synthetic quartz by a process known as hydrothermal crystallization. Since the synthetic stones produced are of excellent quality, it is possible that large-scale domestic production of a synthetic quartz may end this country's dependence on Brazil for a supply of natural quartz.

An antimetabolite compound has been discovered which promises lifelong immunity for fabrics against textile-destroying insects. It can be used to impregnate fabrics during the dye-vat process or be applied in an aqueous solution to existing fabrics in the home.

A system known as APT (Automatically Programed Tool) has been developed for computers to give orders to automatic machines. A human operator can communicate descriptions of required parts and how they should be cut directly to an electronic computer. Improvement and expansion of the system will be under the direction of the Aircraft Industries Association.

Fires and flashovers may be prevented in electrical systems by application of a coat of a new greaselike silicone compound. This same compound, when mixed with graphite, almost eliminates dirt and corrosion from 300-volt direct crane rails and trolleys.

Geography and Geology

What are the four main types of fossils? Which might you expect to find in your area? Where?

How do caves originate? What valuable investigations do speleologists carry out?

Describe the difference in formation of continental and oceanic islands.

Study four different kinds of rocks and discuss differences between them.

Why is the sea becoming more salty?

How do glaciers destroy rocks? What is the result?

Describe sea life during the Cambrian period. How does this knowledge relate to modern science?

After examination of a map of Alaska, can you tell whether the coast is a rising or a sinking coast? What is the cause and significance of such coastal change?

What is the history of the formation of the Appalachian Mountains of today?

What are the various causes of the formation of lakes?

What explorations were made in Africa by the British in the nineteenth century?

Why are sheet floods damaging?

Describe the geysers of the North Island of New Zealand

What is known about the bed cracks of the Atlantic and Indian Oceans?

What causes a seemingly extinct volcano to erupt?

Geophysics

What are the coastal warning displays for the following: (a) small-craft warning, (b) gale warning, (c) whole-gale warning, (d) hurricane warning? What factors cause each of these weather conditions?

How do scientists undertake the study of climate as it was in ages past?

What is the rainiest place in the world and what is its annual average rainfall? Why?

What devices are most in use today for weather forecasting? What new ones are being developed?

Why are the results of rain making from clouds seeded with dry ice or bombarded with silver iodide not always successful?

Look into the effects of climate on health, including such factors as ultraviolet and other irradiation, air and water temperatures, humidity, precipitation and wind. It has been reported recently that small ionized air molecules influence biological behavior.

The U.S. Department of Agriculture is experimenting in the Southwest with possible ways of recovering water normally lost in flash floods. Suggestions include small storage reservoirs, storage of water underground and improved vegetation so as to increase the rate of water infiltration into the soil.

Because the earth's rotation is gradually slowing down, the twenty-four-hour day is two hundredths of a second longer than it was two thousand years ago. The reason for the earth's slowing down is still a mystery.

A method of deciding when and where a storm is forming has been evolved through the application of automatic computing methods; further research extending to other important parts of the earth sciences is needed.

The Committee on Oceanography of the National Academy of Sciences-National Research Council warns that failure to double the intensity of deep-sea research within the next ten years will lead to serious economic, political and military hazards. Such intensification could be accomplished by expansion of the government's support of the marine sciences' basic research activity. This research might include studies of the oceans' mineral and food resources, more accurate prediction and possible control of climate, and improvement of military defenses against attacks by missile-launching submarines.

Can lightning be controlled? The U.S. Weather Bureau and the U. S. Forest Service are conducting experiments by distributing silver iodide from airplanes directly into cloud bases. This may stop or prevent storms. Scientists are also studying thunderheads by radar and testing a simple lightning-stroke counter.

Inventions

The National Inventors Council, serving as a liaison between the civilian inventor and the military, has listed twenty-eight new problems in its *Supplement to Technical Problems Affecting National Defense*. Inventors having solutions to any of these problems are asked to write up their ideas and send them to the Council, U.S. Dept. of Commerce, Wash. 25, D.C. Among the solutions wanted are the following: a Buck Rogers rocket device that can be worn by man to shoot him across rugged land, or to serve as a parachute in airplane trouble; a method for keeping bread from hardening; ways to stabilize muddy soils; a device for measuring the height of large water waves; a better fungicide for clothing; insect repellents that can be impregnated in clothing; a reliable long-life cathode tube.

Mathematics

How does the algebraic concept of *group* help to unify different branches of mathematics.

Explain the words *factor* and *factoring*.

Traditional Euclidian geometry is often attacked today because of its logical imperfections. Why is this so?

What contribution did Dedekind make to the problem of irrational numbers?

Who was the inventor of the computing machine that served as the starting point in the development of mechanical calculation, and in what century did he live?

Why do scientists consider the metric system simpler and more convenient to use than the English system of measurement?

Is every even number, other than 2, the sum of two primes or the sum of a prime and the unit?

Find general rules for flexing patterns in flexagons, relations between the geometrical form of the strip of paper folded and the ways in which the flexagon flexes.

Investigate prime numbers, which occur frequently in pairs, as P and P+2. Is there an infinite number of such pairs, or is there a largest pair of prime numbers with this property?

Can you discover a proof of Fermat's Last Theorem? If n is an integer greater than 2, there do not exist integers x, y, z, all different from zero, such that $x^n - y^n = z^n$. (Fermat wrote that he had discovered a truly remarkable proof, but it has never been rediscovered.)

Prove that the area of a Pythagorean triangle is never equal to a square number.

Demonstrate the impossibility of proving Euclid's parallel postulate.

What is the theory of congruences and how important are its uses?

What is a repeating or recurring decimal? Illustrate.

What is the importance of the "random walk" theory, and how can it be applied practically to scientific and technological problems?

What has been David Hilbert's contribution to the "new mathematics"?

What kinds of arguments are there in mathematics?

What are the meanings of dispersion and measure of dispersion in statistics?

What is the importance of the concept of size (that is, of something being "greater than" another thing) in mathematics? What kinds of mathematics can one do without using this idea?

What are the known methods of computing the actual values of π^π; of e (base of natural logarithms)? Can you think of easier ways? (Note: Measuring things, in a physical science, is cheating here, and bound to be in error, since no physical measurement is exact.)

Computer Science

What ways can you think of for linking together digital computers and analog computers? What applications can you find for systems in which an analog computer performs continuous "computations" which may stray farther and farther from the right results, but receives periodic exact values from a digital computer and resets itself to agree with these accurate values? What advantages would such a system have over a more complex, more accurate pure analog system?

How would you build a device which could examine a photograph and print out a list of the objects appearing in that photograph?

(A simpler problem: Can you design a machine which can take, as input, a picture of a geometrical figure—triangle, square, circle, etc.—and give as output some signal indicating which kind of figure appears in the picture? Try to develop one for which size, position and orientation do not matter.)

One very important problem is that of locating a desired piece of information in a vast library full of books and magazines. This becomes difficult because a fact may appear not in a book on the subject itself, but in one on a related subject.

Investigate the usefulness of the ideas of set theory, topology and symbolic logic in tracing down facts in an organized library. Would computers be useful here?

Try to develop a device (or a program for a digital computer) which will take a collection of English words and combine them to form grammatical sentences. The ultimate purpose is to develop a machine which, given a dictionary, will generate only grammatical sentences, one after another, and which will generate *any* grammatical sentence you choose if you let it run long enough.

Logic

What does the logician mean by the word *paradox*? Find examples. (At a more advanced level: What revisions in logical systems have been proposed to avoid the various paradoxes? How do the paradoxes, and the logical systems which avoid them, affect the validity of proofs of mathematical theorems?)

Medicine

Cooperative research effort on the part of life scientists and electronic engineers could develop the new field of medical electronics to the point where it contributes as much to a comprehension of life processes and medicine as electronics already contributes to the fields of physical research and industrial practice.

Analyze royal jelly, the food fed by bees to future queens of hives. (An antibiotic has been found in the jelly.)

Successful skin transplants with young tadpoles have been accomplished, and further research, supported by the National Institutes of Health, is being carried on with the idea of obtaining better skin grafts in humans.

A glue which is a plastic polyurethane foam has been used successfully in treating leg fractures in 250 trial patients. The foam is poured on broken ends of the bone, the glue stiffens and the patient is able to walk in three days. Distribution of the glue for general use will not be made until further clinical trials prove its utility.

The spectroscope has many possibilities, as yet little explored, in the fields of cell processes and human disease.

Treatment of arthritis and other diseases of the connective tissue in man may be aided by experimentation with tadpoles raised in water containing chemical compounds that cause tumors and lesions.

The "shotgun" program to discover a drug to cure cancer, as well as basic studies into the nature of the disease, have as yet failed to solve most of its problems. For instance, why do supposedly successful treatments not guarantee against a flare-up of the disease, and why do some people have the power to resist the disease? Many scientific and medical men believe that the answer lies somewhere in the laws that govern cell growth.

How may we be protected against contamination from radioactive fall-out? This is not only a problem for the future, for high contamination levels in wheat and milk have been found. It is possible that the Public Health Service may be given responsibility for setting and enforcing radiation safety standards, as this agency is already involved in maintaining a national surveillance network of water, air and milk, and it has a program for educating the public concerning the problem of radiation.

Can a lamp improve human health and moods? The Westinghouse Electric Corporation has come up with a lamp producing negative air ions, which is being tested for installation into air conditioners and heating systems, with the purpose of bringing relief to asthma, hay fever and sinus sufferers, depressed persons and possibly victims of other diseases.

Work with fragments of the mitochondrial membrane from cell protoplasm convinces scientists that this membrane plays an essential role in the exchange of electrons needed for energy storage and release. Further research is being conducted to determine the exact structure of the mitochondrial membrane parts and how they function.

A serious public health problem is presented with the increasing use of detergents by the housewife, since they make a complete circle from the kitchen sink back to the sink via the water tap. Filter and other water purification means do not remove them, and there is need for gaining data on a long-term basis as to their physiological effect A simple test for their detection in household water is to watch for foaming at the tap.

Medicine today is still in a relatively primitive stage, with respect to outdated tools in a doctor's black bag, nondiscovery of the reasons why certain drugs work and lack of information about the molecular structure of body cells. New discoveries and the devising of new instruments are needed in combatting many diseases and in preventing them from recurring.

The plumlike fruit of the gingko tree has for centuries been thought to have a curative effect on cancer. The National Cancer Institute has scheduled this fruit, along with hundreds of other plant forms, for intensive laboratory tests in order to discover any scientific basis for the supposed cures.

A recent study shows that the reaction to mosquito bites is an allergic one and not the result of the insect's injecting poison that irritates the skin. The allergenic substance, limited to the head-thorax region of the mosquito, is complex; there is evidence against its being a single, simple chemical compound.

Electronic devices applied to the field of medicine have already proved of inestimable aid in diagnosis, treatment and surgery. In use at the present time are devices that make blood counts, record brain waves, detect cysts, radio information from the stomach, watch chemicals do work in human cells and substitute for heart, lung and kidney functions. There are endless possibilities for future research work, such as electronic substitutes functioning on a permanent basis to replace defective organs, and various devices for the blind.

According to a Russian scientist who tested dogs, increase

in the amount and acidity of gastric juice in the stomach of the dog may be caused by sound waves too high to be heard by the human ear.

What is the role of RNA (ribonucleic acid) in skin grafts?

What are the advantages and disadvantages in using cadaver blood in transfusions?

Wht are some of the important facts and questions contained in *Problems in the Evaluation of Carcinogenic Hazard from Use of Food Additives,* issued by the Food Protection Committee of the National Academy of Sciences-National Research Council?

Dentistry

Of what use are human wisdom teeth?

Using modern biological laboratory techniques such as the electron microscope and tooth-and-bone-seeking radioisotopes, answers are being sought to such vital questions as: How do teeth and bones develop? How does saliva affect teeth? How do germs and teeth give clues to bodily health and biological aging? How do certain rare food elements affect oral conditions? (See *Science,* 130: 1681, 1960.)

Can you help to find a very much better substitute for so-called silicate fillings for front teeth? The present silicate material is comparatively brittle and soluble, does not make a real bond with the tooth, requires the sacrifice of a too-large area of healthy tooth to provide anchorage of the filling, must be replaced in less than five years. (See *Science,* 130: 1681, 1960.)

Information is needed on the causes of gingivitis and pyorrhea, common in later life as a cause of inflamed gums, loose teeth, destruction of jawbone. (See *Science,* 130: 1681, 1960.)

Twenty years of experimentation have shown the influence of heredity in tooth decay of rats, and investigation now centers on discovering the hereditary process in man which relates to cavities.

Studies reported by a Texas dentist indicate that people in the habit of grinding their teeth while under emotional stress can so damage their gums as to lead to a loss of teeth. Damage to the teeth does not occur during the chewing habits and a broad group of habits such as pipe smoking or process but is the result of habit neuroses, occupational opening bottle caps with the teeth.

Results of experiments over a two-year period with apple-eating children convinced a British dentist that the apple eaters presented only half the amount of tooth decay and one third the number of gum disorders of the control group. The fruit was served in unpeeled slices after each meal and following snacks.

Follow up the findings that phosphorus in Texas corn and milk prevent tooth decay. Relate to fluorine in water, etc.

Experimentation with hamsters fed on Texan corn and milk has proved that the extra phosphorus thus supplied led to forty percent less tooth decay. Use of four times the amount of phosphorus has resulted in a hundred percent effectiveness in the teeth of hamsters.

After stimulation, how long does it take the human eye to start activities leading to muscle response?

Mineral Industries and Mineralogy

Trace the uses of asphalt from ancient times to the present day.

What are the chief sources of the earth's marble, and for what is it used chiefly today?

Describe present conditions of the diamond mining industry in the Union of South Africa.

Trace the history of the uses of petroleum from ancient times to the present.

What are the advantages and disadvantages of using steel for building purposes?

Discuss the locations of the world's best coal supplies.

Patents

If you have invented something, how and why do you go about getting a patent for it?

Investigate a window that traps radiation for purposes of heating or power generation. The window may be adjusted to follow the course of the sun, but this may also be accomplished in a stationary position by a series of lenses that focus the rays in the trap. Patent 2,888,007.

Consider a device for reducing ghost images on television screens. This device is situated between the transmitter and receiver and would intercept the delay signal. Patent 2,888,515.

A daylight-controlled on-off switch for headlights saves

the driver from switching automobile headlights on and off. Patent 2,888,611.

Photography

Of what materials are good photographic filters made? What others might prove effective?

What is the purpose of an exposure meter and how do you use it? Can you improve on the design and simplicity of use?

Is it necessary to have a 3-D camera to take stereo pictures?

Physics

How in modern life is the primitive method of friction and a spark used to produce fire?

What acoustical problems are evident in a theatre that is only half full, in comparison with one enjoying a capacity audience? How might these problems be solved?

Look into the new tunnel diode which may ultimately replace the transistor in tiny radios and computers. (It is being produced in limited quantities for research.)

Look into the use of an electron beam for magnetic writing which has proved successful and especially suited for electronic computers.

Investigate photogrammetric charting methods that can produce exact reproductions of cultural and historical objects, as proved by demonstrations at the Ethnological Museum of Sweden.

Explain the lack of agreement between the observed and predicted position of Jupiter, which suggests that Newton's theory of gravitation, used to predict planet motion, may be wrong.

What new applications can you think of using semi-conductor-like materials being developed in solid state physics research? (Luminescent and photoconductive materials are being used in models of picture-thin television sets and luminescent walls for rooms. Transistors already are in use in hearing aids, tiny radios, etc.)

Work continues on developing electronic systems for increasing the sensitivity of telescopes.

A computer-linked system for measuring star positions is under development.

Work is being done on interpreting radio signals from sun,

moon and certain planets, from more distant objects in the Milky Way and from star systems beyond the Milky Way.

Through "particle physics," a search is being made for the order that pervades the physical world; but in spite of the mass of findings, no obvious conclusions have been reached.

A new theory has been evolved which states that the secret of the structure of liquids is organized irregularity. An attempt has been made to demonstrate this in a physical model and to explain this model in mathematical terms. The conclusion drawn is that the basic property of a liquid, its fluidity, can be most easily understood in terms of the packing of irregular polyhedra, as in a foam. By experiments the commonly accepted view that a gas and a liquid form a single fluid phase has been contradicted; they are distant states of matter. If these theories prove to be realistic, there may be practical applications in the fields of refrigeration, gas-liquid separation and the flow of liquids.

A flat loudspeaker with a thin membrane having an electric circuit printed on it has been developed in Israel. This membrane, which replaces the paper core, vibrates to and fro in a magnetic field created by thin strips of powerful ferrite magnets.

An electronic music synthesizer has been installed at Columbia University for a program of composition and research in electronic music. The machine is a system of electronic circuits that can generate all of the characteristics of any audible tone and can produce sounds like those of any known instrument.

Measurement of waves that cause a one-inch electric spark has been made possible by use of an "electric eye" and new ultra-fast measuring equipment.

Scientists are trying to find a method of establishing the age of military and other supplies, particularly those in storage, by measuring the amount of radiation from known radioactive materials in the items.

How can radioactive fall-out from atom bomb tests be used to expose new sources of drinking water?

What are the principles involved in heat transfer?

How may workmen in industrial plants be protected from radiant heat?

Define the term *vacuum-distillation camera* and explain its value.

Where is the ground concentration of strontium 90 fall-out

from nuclear explosions higher—at the base of slopes or on hilltop areas?

What controls pitch in music?

What is hydraulic paradox and how can it function in measuring?

The armed services want a device that can be built into a man's suit to distribute heat over his body in subzero weather. The device must operate without a restricting power source and must operate eight hours without refueling; it must permit rapid discarding, must not hamper agility, must be reasonably lightweight and fully reliable.

Biophysics

Studies of the human brain may show scientists the way to build better computers, just as studies of the beetle's eye have provided a wiring diagram for a new type of absolute airspeed indicator, and experiments in training octopuses have led to the development of a machine with a capacity, approaching that of the octopus, to perceive and remember shapes.

Psychology

Investigate humor as a safety valve for hospital patients. Anxiety, submission to hospital authority, gripes about food, etc., have been found to yield to humor, especially when supplied by the patients themselves.

Explore recent research in the field of mind-body reactions, such as learning to avoid annoying noises; the effect of deafness on people taking the Rorschach test of personality; the perception of depth on the part of creeping babies; the future space traveler's ability to hear, no matter what his position in his capsule; a remedy for the deterioration of efficiency in a lookout by means of artificial signals; the faster beat of the human heart caused by electric shock and a buzzer.

Investigate the possibilities of teaching Interlingua, the international language, in junior high school as a useful introduction to other languages. (This is being done in Dighton, Kansas.)

Study behavior in social groups through participant observation.

What is consciousness, and what are the reasons for its existence?

What accounts for man's agelong concern with the super-natural?

An experiment has been made with ciphers which fall into three major classifications: concealment, transposition and substitution. These methods can be combined in a cipher, making the cryptographer's task even more difficult.

A Canadian physician reports that colds provide some people with a harmless emotional outlet which should not be repressed or worse psychic harm might result.

What makes a young engineer successful? Studies involving about 1200 engineers showed that the ability to form 3-dimensional special images and a knowledge of advanced engineering were important factors.

Have the skills developed by the armed forces during the compulsory military training period proved of later use to the youth involved?

Under what circumstances could a person's vocabulary deteriorate?

In the field of psychology, what is a functionalist?

What other qualities are needed besides high intelligence test scores for students to achieve success?

What is the Draw-A-Man test and how is it used?

How can you improve your speed in reading?

Do dogs have a sense of humor?

LET'S suppose you have finished polishing a satisfying piece of work. Or it might be more realistic to suppose that you have reached a natural stopping point where it becomes evident that new thinking, planning and equipment may be necessary before you can go any further.

You may have carried out this project to pin down an answer that eluded you. If you had fun looking for that answer, or if you actually produced what scientists and mathematics call an "elegant proof," you will be wondering now how you can share it and check its validity against other work in your field.

One of the most rewarding ways to do this is by entering your project in one of the local or national competitions for young student-scientists. Descriptions of some of these are included here. For details, rules, entry materials and other information, consult your science teacher, club sponsor or other adult leader, or write to the addresses given.

Science Fairs

What Is a Science Fair?

A science fair is a collection of exhibits, each of which is designed to show a biological, chemical, physical or technical principle, a laboratory or other procedure, an industrial development or an orderly collection of anything which can be fitted into the broad concept of any branch of any pure or applied science.

Every year millions of people see science exhibits shown by students at science fairs leading to the National Science Fair-International.

The simplest fair is an exhibition of science projects held in the school itself, where all the experiments, collections and displays that have been worked out by students either in class or as extracurricular science club activities are shown. These fairs have become so numerous that it is difficult to keep track of them. They often are a feature of a meeting or a showing to which the public is invited.

If the scientists who judge the science fair agree that a

piece of work is valid and is well presented, the exhibitor may find himself winning an award and taking his project on to a large regional fair. City-wide, area or regional science fairs may exhibit several hundred projects in a large hall and may be visited by thousands of interested people.

Those chosen as finalists may exhibit at the National Science Fair-International, conducted each year by Science Service. The National Science Fair-International has developed from a beginning of 13 affiliated area fairs in 1950 to 193 in 1960.

The scope of projects has done some growing too. The once-upon-a-time exhibit of several casually mounted butterfly specimens has given way to expert demonstrations and really mature research work. Since the present generation keeps up very well with the latest developments, many a professional scientist has been amazed to see the newest design in artificial kidneys or computers or rockets very competently exhibited at a science fair. These are not just models, copied from drawings. They involve considerable understanding of the principles and sometimes include new features designed by the exhibitor. If it is a winning project, some work has been done with the equipment once it was built.

The rules of the National Science Fair-International specify that to be eligible boys and girls must be students in the last three years of public, private, parochial or other secondary schools, and must have been selected for highest honors in a regional fair affiliated with the National Science Fair-International.

Each affiliated fair is entitled to send two finalists and their exhibits to the National Science Fair-International, paying their expenses and undertaking responsibility for them.

For National Science Fair-International Awards, exhibits are judged in the two general categories of biological and physical sciences, and the exhibits of girl and boy finalists are judged separately. First place awards are made to the top boy's and girl's projects in each of two categories. Other awards are prorated according to the number of girls and boys among the finalists, regardless of the category of their exhibits.

A project may continue and expand work that has been exhibited at a previous fair. However, *identical* repetition of a project automatically disqualifies a finalist.

Each finalist receives a rainbow-ribboned gold and silver medal engraved with his or her name and that of the cooperating organization. A facsimile medal on a certificate is sent to the principal of the school of each finalist to become a trophy in the school.

On the basis of critical judging, outstanding finalists are given "Wish Awards"—selected scientific equipment, materials or books which winners have "wished for" to help them in their study and experimentation.

Also given at the National Science Fair-International are Award Citations and honorable mentions from the American Medical Association for the best exhibits in the broad field of medical sciences and health. Award Citations carry with them all-expense-paid trips to the annual meeting of the AMA.

Certificates of Superior Achievement, and invitations to exhibit at the annual meeting of the American Dental Association, are awarded to selected finalists whose exhibits are considered best in the broad field of science related to dentistry. Certificates of Meritorious Achievement, plus gift certificates toward purchase of scientific equipment, are given to winners of honorable mentions.

A plaque and an invitation to exhibit at the annual American Veterinary Medical Association meeting are awarded in this field. Alternates also may be recognized and honored.

The American Pharmaceutical Association offers a First Award of an engraved plaque and an all-expense-paid trip to the annual meeting of the American Pharmaceutical Association in Washington, D.C. A Second Award winner also is designated.

The American Chemical Society presents First Awards of plaques and gifts of money for the purchase of science materials. Alternate Awards also are given.

The American Heart Association awards a citation plaque for the best heart related exhibit and a trip to the annual AHA meeting to exhibit the winner's project.

The Society of American Bacteriologists make First and Second Awards of plaques and money for scientific equipment.

The American Institute of Biological Sciences makes awards to top exhibitors in its field, inviting the winners to attend the annual meeting of the Institute.

The Optical Society of America makes an award in the fields related to optics.

Additional professional organizations are planning to honor outstanding work in their specialties.

U.S. Navy judges honor finalists whose exhibits are considered best in the broad area of Navy-oriented projects. Each fall these finalists join other Navy Science Cruisers (one selected from each regional affiliated fair) for a highly science-oriented trip on fleet ships at sea.

U.S. Army and the Association of the U.S. Army judges honor finalists whose exhibits are in the specialized areas of missiles, satellites, electronics, electronic calculators, mathematics, high and low temperatures, instrumentation, meteorology and medicine. Winners of Army Science Awards are given trips to Army science installations.

U.S. Air Force judges select outstanding exhibits in various categories, including air power and air explorations. Finalists receive recognition and appear with their exhibits at the annual Aerospace Panorama Exposition.

Educators and newsmen cooperating in the program of the National Science Fair-International plan the fair in a different city each year.

All finalists enjoy a four-day program of scientific sightseeing and meetings with leading scientists. They become acquainted with other finalists having similar interests, compare their work and share their enthusiasm.

Judging is based on creative ability, scientific thought, thoroughness, skill, clarity and the dramatic value of each exhibit. Scientists designated by Science Service judge the contest, and the decision of these judges is final in all cases.

How to Conduct a Science Fair

The science club sponsor or teacher, or group of sponsors or teachers, first should get permission from the principal or board of education to hold a science fair to which parents and the public will be invited.

The fair may be designed for operation in one school, or each school of a group of schools can schedule the event to occur substantially at the same time. The best exhibits may then be presented at a final centralized place.

Fairs should be held early in the spring. If entry is arranged for finalists to participate in the National Science Fair-International, the regional fair must close early in April. Names of finalists must be reported immediately to the National Science Fair-International Headquarters, at the close of the regional fair.

Regional fairs may be held in classrooms in school, in the chemistry or physics laboratories, in the school gymnasium or cafeteria, in a community building, college building, museum or armory. In fact, any place where adequate electric current facilities are available and which will accommodate crowds will prove satisfactory. If held in a hall, local police and fire departments should be advised of the event so that guards can be posted to protect the properties adequately. School events should be monitored for protection and to guide people to and from the exhibit areas.

School fairs may be open to students in any year of elementary or secondary school, from kindergarten up, if desired. Exhibits should be so arranged and classified that all those made by students of one grade division may be compared both by the judges and the public. Each exhibit may be made by a group of students or only one student. Group exhibits should be judged apart from those made by individuals.

In the upper grades all physics exhibits should be grouped into a class separate from those in chemistry, or biology. The committee should set the limits defined by educational levels, not by age of the student.

Judges should be people who understand the topic being judged or can approach it open-mindedly. A good combination is a layman, a teacher from the same grade but from another school and a scientist for each division or classification —the layman to tell if he learned something from the exhibit, the teacher to specify if the exhibit represents good work on the part of the student of the specified school year and the scientist to attest to its technical accuracy. Point scores are recommended. Judges should evaluate exhibits before the show is open to the public.

Anything from a silver star or rubber stamp to more elaborate awards may be made. Often merely the posting of merits will suffice. All exhibits and names of exhibitors, schools, etc., should appear in a list of exhibits. Local townsmen, civic, scientific or cultural groups or industry may present awards. If they are other than certificates, they should be selected so as to further the scientific education of the winners. School plaques or certificates also may be given. Scholarships, if available, should be awarded for scholastic attainments as well as good exhibits.

What has been stated for a school science fair applies to a regional or city-wide fair, except that greater numbers are involved and greater attention will be given to each operation.

Regional and school science fairs generally use the rules of the National Science Fair-International or adapt them to fit various local situations.

Depending on local rules, students may work individually or in groups. Exhibits must be designed and made by students. They may seek help from educators and others. Each exhibit should be so arranged that it can be understood by the layman without requiring an accompanying demonstration or lecture. Judgment of exhibits is based on work done by students, not on cost of accessory or incidental equipment.

Exhibiting Your Science Project

Before you even begin work on a project that you plan to enter in a science fair, you will want to have some idea of how it might be exhibited effectively. More detailed ideas will occur to you as your work progresses, and you will want to jot these down for future use.

When you are ready to build the exhibit, first make a preliminary design to see what the over-all effect will be. Then make a more accurate sketch that includes all necessary details.

1. Layout. A science fair exhibit for most fairs should be forty-eight inches wide by thirty inches front to back, or less. Some things, such as telescopes, which may not fit into these dimensions, should be displayed so that their longest dimension extends vertically, to avoid crowding by neighboring exhibits.

Starting with sections of a corrugated pasteboard box and sheets of cardboard the required size, rough in the space your exhibit is to occupy. The floor and the back wall of this exhibit space will hold the most important objects to be shown. Remember that material or lettering high on the back wall has the best chance of being seen by the visitors, many of whom will be peering over the shoulders of others in front of them.

Try to proportion the various objects in your exhibit so that they can be seen clearly from where the visitors will stand. Too many large objects will make the space look cluttered. Too few small ones will seem lost.

If your idea is to show one compact object or group and label the parts, bright-colored ribbons or adhesive tape may lead the eye from the part, located in the center foreground of the exhibit space, to a wall area where the explanation is lettered large enough to be read from a distance. Side walls used for this purpose may slope from the narrower back panel toward the wider front edge of the enclosing walls.

Successive steps in a processing story may be labeled in a similar fashion and numbered from one on, reading preferably from left to right.

2. Types of Exhibits. There are three basic methods of treatment, with many variations for each. The first is "breadboard" style, that is, on an open breadboard, or flat on the exhibit tables. The second is the panel form of construction in which sides, back and base are put to use. Sometimes even the top and front also become parts of the exhibit area. The third method utilizes boxed units set one alongside the other, and sometimes on top of each other as well.

The breadboard style is suited to the display of large mounted specimens, chemical and physical apparatus, objects under magnifiers and microscopes, models, industrial replicas, experimental electrical circuits, growing plants and the like. To prepare such a display for speedy setup, designate where all the parts are to be exhibited on a piece of wrapping paper cut to the size of the space allowed. With heavy pencil outline the base of each object on the paper. Number each article and number the diagram as well. Pack all the parts in a box, preferably divided by cardboard partitions.

In panel construction, take full advantage of the side panels, base and back by treating each as a separate unit. If possible, construct the exhibit area of a sturdy material like pressed wood, plywood or wallboard. Easiest to use is pegboard, with its predrilled holes. Arrange a system for coupling the panels together, perhaps by lashing them with shoestring, cord or tape, or by using hinges and removable pins.

If your specimens are flat or are to be mounted against the panels, the panels can be hinged with cloth hinges, like a folding screen. Probably the best way is to couple the pieces together with loose pin hinges. Stand the panels in the positions they are to occupy and screw the hinges to the backs so that the parts are held securely together. Knock out the pins and the pieces come apart. Hooks or screw eyes may be driven into the panels to support hanging specimen materials, or holes for brackets can be made in sides or back. Large specimens can be wired to the panels with little danger of their coming undone.

Completely boxed-in units are recommended for such things as radio transmitters, receivers, amplifiers, oscilloscopes, numerous valuable or fragile specimens and, of course, aquaria and Wardian cases, natural habitat groups and the like. Where a number of electrical interconnections must be made, avoid single wire connectors and use multiple pin type plugs and connectors instead.

Aquaria should not be cleared for transport. Instead, remove the fish and place them in transport cans or put a few in each of a number of cardboard containers. Syphon the water into gallon jugs. Cover the plants with wet newspaper or paper towels. At the exhibit area return the same water by pouring it onto the paper so as not to disturb the soil or gravel. Then remove paper and return the fish. The tank will remain clear.

Plants in Wardian cases or natural habitat displays are easy to transport if kept in individual pots sunk into the surrounding surface deep enough so that the rims do not show. Then they can be removed to make the case lighter and reset without danger to growth. Plants must pass federal and state quarantine regulations.

It is helpful to make a small diagram to follow on setup day. Such a guide will allow you to assemble your exhibit in little time.

3. Lettering and Labels. Avoid huge letters poorly made, ponderous charts or diagrams, notebook records spread across the table top. Make your major legends small and neat and readable at a distance of six to eight feet. Judges and visitors who want to study the details can leaf through your notebook, which preferably should be secured to the right front edge of your exhibit space.

Various precut letters, lettering guides and aids are available from drafting supplies stores. Small and large plastic letters from discarded display material often can be obtained from stores and restaurants. Thin strips of colored cellophane and masking tape attached to a background may also be used.

Letters from magazines and newspapers are useful for shape, size and style. They may be traced by moistening a sheet of good bond paper with lighter fluid, which makes the paper transparent, then tracing the letters with a pencil. Because of the fire hazard, keep flames away and work in a well-ventilated room. When the fluid evaporates, the paper will resume its opacity.

Prepare the text of your legends carefully. Write what you want to say, then set it aside for a day or two. When you go over it again, you may find useless words that you can eliminate, or you may want to reword some of it to make it clearer or more interesting.

4. Safe and Sturdy Construction. A science fair exhibit must be designed to protect visitors from possible accident and exhibit material from careless handling from the occasional souvenir hunter. Exhibits must be durably and safely designed and constructed, using approved switches and cords for 110-volt operation.

To avoid accidents, science fairs ban strong acids and alkalies, flames, explosives, materials liable to spontaneous combustion, dangerous gases, poisons, poisonous reptiles, cultures of disease germs and other materials which the Fair Committee judges to be potentially harmful.

This does not mean that a research project involving one or more of these materials is barred, but only that the actual material must not be placed where visitors might come in contact with it.

Always substitute safe and permanent materials for dangerous or unstable ones. Avoid top-heavy structures or insecurely fastened display boards, electrical insulation of doubtful quality or make-do support of heavy equipment.

If there is any doubt in your mind about the adequacy of your construction, reinforce it *before* you take it to the science fair.

Regulations for Experiments with Animals

This guide for high school students of biology was prepared at the request of Science Clubs of America by a committee of the National Society for Medical Research and later amended by committees of the Animal Care Panel and Institute of Laboratory Animal Resources.

1. The basic aim of scientific studies that involve animals is to achieve an understanding of life, and to advance our knowledge of life processes. Such studies lead to a respect for life.

2. A qualified adult supervisor must assume primary responsibility for the purposes and conditions of any experiment that involves living animals.

3. No experiment should be undertaken that involves anesthetic drugs, surgical procedures, pathogenic organisms, toxicological products, carcinogens or radiation unless a trained biological scientist, physician, dentist or veterinarian directly supervises the experiment.

4. Any experiment must be performed with the animal under appropriate anesthesia if pain is involved.

5. The comfort of the animal used in any study shall be a prime concern of the student investigator. Gentle handling, proper feeding and provision of appropriate sanitary quarters shall at all times be strictly observed. Any experiment in nutritional deficiency may proceed only to the point where symptoms of the deficiency appear. Appropriate measures shall then be taken to correct the deficiency, if such action is feasible.

6. Students shall not be permitted to participate in science fairs held under the auspices of the National Science Fair-International until their adult sponsors have submitted assurance in writing that the above rules have been observed.

The Rewards of Science Fairs

Students who exhibit their projects at science fairs discover that, whether or not they are declared winners, they take home less tangible rewards which they will value for the rest of their lives.

They mention such important gains as new self-confidence and self-respect, satisfaction in having planned and carried through a productive piece of work, familiarity with the many ways of searching out information, contact with likeminded students and adult scientists and experience in discussing their ideas, work and plans with other people. In addition to all this, most science fair exhibitors collect a whole hatful of stimulating new ideas and fresh perspectives.

The experience of doing an independent project and of the contacts with other science-minded students and mature scientists often has started a chain reaction of enthusiasm. Many students have learned, to their own surprise, what ability they have in science. Suddenly they want very much to study science and mathematics courses, looking forward to college training in one of the sciences or in science and math teaching. Those who already were eager science-aspirants have become more convinced than ever that they have chosen an exciting and rewarding career.

It is evident that science fair experience in itself is an important ingredient in the development of young scientists. For instance, in a Science Service poll 121 National Science Fair-International finalists were asked, "What did designating you as a finalist mean to you?"

About a third of the students felt that the stimulation of such personal gratification was important. One fifth said that receiving public recognition was a valuable experience. About a tenth each answered, "Responsibility for future effort," "improved status for the future" and "increased self-confidence."

Participating in science fairs also can teach a student the somewhat elusive technique of winning and losing well, that is, without undue puffing up or abject collapse. Both teachers and students report that winning some recognition has a way of inspiring further trying, sometimes followed by even greater achievement. In fact, some students say that their interest in training for a career in science or technology began when they earned an honor or an award at a science fair. Science fair directors and judges like to remember, also, the instances when losing showed that an exhibitor had what it took, stimulating him to develop really excellent work habits and attitudes and the drive to do better the next time.

Teachers and parents say that in planning and putting together a project a student discovers ways of finding answers —through books, magazines, scientific papers and his own experiments—that can enrich all the rest of his life, whatever his eventual career.

Boys and girls discover, too, that being part of a fair brings them into contact with other searching minds, both in their own generation and among educators and working scientists. Many a teen-ager who had felt "different" and lonely has confessed that such contacts with like minds was an unexpected and immensely gratifying experience.

Many exhibitors say that continued science fair activity has helped them to find ways of communicating facts and hunches, and the way they feel about both, to other people. Educators agree that such ability is rather sadly rare among scientists and thinkers of all kinds, and even among teachers.

Success Stories

The announcement of the 1958 Nobel Prize in Medicine and Physiology revealed a particularly inspiring success story of a scientist who started out in a high school science club and science fair. Co-winner Joshua Lederberg was an active member of the Stuyvesant High School Science Club in New York City some twenty years ago. The Nobelist says that he feels greatly indebted to the unusual opportunities given to him as a high school student and believes that such early encouragement is highly important and valuable.

Science Clubs of America has kept a file on each of 760 Science Talent Search winners and nearly 1500 National Science Fair-International finalists. These files and follow-up studies are yielding impressive statistics on the progress of promising students toward professional success.

For example, 100% of the Science Talent Search winners have attended or now are attending college, with all but a handful majoring in some branch of science. Of those old enough, nearly half have received or soon will receive doctoral degrees.

Winners are on the faculties of colleges and universities here and abroad (one is a college president), conducting research, teaching or both; on the staffs of industrial research laboratories and organizations; on research staffs of government institutions or endowed research organizations; and so on.

Careers in the physical sciences have attracted the largest number so far, with physics ranking somewhat ahead of chemistry and mathematics. The second largest number are working in the biological sciences and medicine. Engineering has claimed the third largest number of winners.

Although as a group the National Science Fair-International finalists are considerably younger than the Science Talent Search winners, they also are demonstrating the validity of the recognition they were given, and in many cases the results of their science club and science fair opportunities. Of those who have reported having received their bachelor's degrees, ninety-five percent majored in science or education. Better than ninety percent of the undergraduates reporting have chosen majors in science or education.

Dr. Dominic B. Edelen, who was one of the finalists in the very first National Science Fair in 1950, is a shining example of what may become of high school scientists honored at the national event.

This twenty-seven-year-old research mathematician is head of the Dynamics Group on Project Vanguard at The Martin Company in Baltimore, Maryland, and has been responsible for analyzing control problems arising from the complex movements of the satellite launching rockets before and during flight. He also is a visiting lecturer at Drexel Institute, Philadelphia, and some of his papers on mathematics have been published. Other papers he has written on missile system analysis are still classified.

The winning project that Dominic took to the National Science Fair ten years ago was a Van de Graaff generator using an accelerator tube he had improvised. This project won a third prize in physical science.

His interest since then has ranged through such problems as the Fourier heat conduction equation and the elastic wave equations. His doctoral dissertation was "The Extension of the Theory of Canonical Maps for a System of Tensorial Partial Differential Equations Which Arise from the Calculus of Variations in Independent Variables."

In addition to providing future-making experience to students, science fairs are a lively spring tonic to science-mindedness, prepared for and looked forward to by the whole community. Even the smallest fry are eager fair visitors who stand on tiptoe to look at protozoa through a microscope or listen delightedly to the roar of a tornado vortex model.

The fairs give young students, their parents, their teachers and all other people who have advised and encouraged them the pleasant and stimulating reward of public recognition. A special side of this is described by Mary Ploog Dankleff, a 1954 National Science Fair finalist from the Northeast Iowa Science Fair, who now has completed college and is married to an English instructor.

"Science fair recognition on the high school level is one of the few ways by which a girl has an equal opportunity to prove her worth," she says. "Each time a girl does receive such recognition she widens a bit the opportunities for herself and other women, and she persuades teachers and employers to give her the opportunity to train professionally in the area of science."

Suzan Lynn Hopkins, another Iowa winner and a 1956 National Science Fair finalist, says that her desire for a career in research was not "simply because I happened to be fortunate enough to win first place in the science fair. I would have done so had I received no recognition at all.

"Anyone who enters a science fair hoping to win a prize," comments Suzan, "really has a distorted sense of values. The experience and knowledge one gains from working on a project outweighs by far any material awards or recognition he might receive."

A premedical student at the University of Iowa, Suzan looks forward to a degree in medicine and further graduate work in chemistry. Eli Lilly and Company, pharmaceutical manufacturers, became interested in Suzan and her science fair project on antibiotics and, as a result, Suzan has worked in the Lilly antibiotic laboratories each summer.

Science project activities and science fairs are considered vitally important to the nation's future by President Eisenhower and top government officials. The United States Navy, Army and Air Force have organized programs to give extensive help and support to student-scientists and to honor outstanding projects at the National Science Fair-International.

There is, in fact, a sort of gigantic Project Protégé going on all over the United States. Without any publicity, and even without very much notice or appreciation from the rest of us, hundreds of highly competent specialists in industry, universities, government and other organizations are nurturing would-be scientists who are still in junior and senior high school.

Uncounted hours of advice, pieces of hard-to-get equipment and unpublished reports have been made available to students by busy scientists who often defer their own work or leisure to help a young person on his way. Immeasurable enthusiasm and dedication have been exchanged in the process, to the mutual benefit of everyone involved.

The Science Talent Search

What Is the Science Talent Search?

Many students in junior high school and in the early years of senior high school look forward to and prepare for entering the Science Talent Search for the Westinghouse Science Scholarships and Awards when they reach their senior year of high school. With essential educational cooperation, students whose scientific skill, talent and ability indicate potential creative originality are discovered through this competition. Science club and science fair activities have proved to be excellent preparation and background for success in this scholarship competition.

The Science Talent Search is conducted annually by Science Clubs of America, as an activity of Science Service, and is sponsored by the Westinghouse Educational Foundation, an organization endowed by the Westinghouse Electric Corporation for the purpose of promoting education and science. It is open to boys and girls who are seniors in public, private or parochial schools in the United States, but excluding U.S. possessions, who are expected by the certifying school officials to complete college entrance qualifications before the following October. Students must not have competed in any previous Science Talent Search.

All the selection techniques of the Science Talent Search for the Westinghouse Science Scholarships and Awards, conducted for nineteen years by Science Clubs of America, have been developed to discover and encourage the most promising young research scientists among the nation's high school seniors.

Scores on the Science Aptitude Examination represent the first hurdle in the judging procedures. There is no predetermined "passing" grade and scores are plotted on a curve to discover which contestants may be qualified for further judging. The qualifying score for boys in the Nineteenth Search was 143; for girls it was 130. This method of scoring allowed a large margin, for the highest score among the boys was 211 out of a total possible score of 244. Highest score among the girls, who made up 22% of the entrants, was 198.

As the next step, detailed scholastic records of each of the students who passed the examination were evaluated. Then evidence presented by the student and by his faculty sponsor concerning his activities, drives, hobbies, personality traits and attitudes was weighed carefully to find any of a number of combinations of achievement and promise.

Each entrant is required to submit a written report of an individual research project, usually consisting of a thousand or so words of text, plus relevant diagrams, theorems, pictures, etc. The papers of all students who had survived the first hurdles of the Search were read critically by a board of professional scientists which included specialists in the many fields explored by the student-scientists. This board worked its way through everything from an idea for a flat video display panel for television to the use of dithioacids to trace esterification reactions with primary, secondary and tertiary alcohols.

Then these professional opinions were added to the other evidence for and against each candidate.

Correlating all of these evaluations, the board of judges

selected an Honors Group of 448 students (10% of those with complete entries) who showed outstanding scientific potential and who were recommended to colleges and universities for admission and scholarship aid.

To choose the forty top winners from this Honors Group, each detail was re-examined and weighed on an even more precise scale of values. During the five-day Science Talent Institute held early in March in Washington, D.C., the known data on each of these forty was supplemented significantly by personal interviews and weighed again in selecting the five who were awarded Westinghouse Science Scholarships. These ranged from $7500 to $3000.

Some of the traits and abilities most prominent among these outstanding young people were intense intellectual curiosity, ingenuity, self-discipline, wide scope of interest and an intuitive grasp of why and how facts may relate to each other.

During the Science Talent Institute the forty winners met eminent scientists, visited scientific laboratories of unusual interest and were interviewed by the judges. The Westinghouse scholarships and awards were announced at a banquet at the close of the Institute.

The 5 scholarships of $7500, $6000, $5000, $4000 and $3000 may be used at any accredited college or university and will help to assure these young pre-scientists of professional training in their fields. Recognition in the Science Talent Search brings many thousands of dollars in other scholarship offers to the Honors Group. In addition, 36 states and the District of Columbia conduct State Science Talent Searches in cooperation with Science Clubs of America, awarding some $600,000 in scholarships to students from their states who are qualified entrants in the national Search.

Entering the Science Talent Search

To enter the Science Talent Search the senior takes the Science Aptitude Examination in his own school under the supervision of his sponsor, teacher or other authorized school official. Such persons also prepare recommendations and see that the scholastic record is transmitted. The student writes a report of about 1000 words on his science project. This should involve original work. Entrants should develop a project that is planned for the Search or adapt to the Search something they already are doing.

Science teachers and school officials qualified to administer the examination may request entry materials for any number of eligible students. Entry blanks are mailed from Washington about November 15. The examination must be administered early in December.

Complete entry materials must reach headquarters of Science Clubs of America in Washington, D.C., by midnight, December 27.

Girls as well as boys are encouraged to enter the Science Talent Search. The number of girls chosen for honors is determined by the proportion of girls who complete entries.

The Science Aptitude Examination

To give you a clue to your possible score on the Science Aptitude Examination of the Science Talent Search, some sample questions from the nineteenth test are presented here for you to try. The full-length examination is intended to pass only the best of the competing students, and no one ever has made a perfect score in the two-and-one-half-hour test.

According to the authors of the annual aptitude examination—Dr. Harold A. Edgerton, New York consulting psychologist, and Dr. Steuart Henderson Britt of Northwestern University—its various parts are designed to measure "ability to think and reason in terms of scientific concepts and vocabulary."

Allow yourself twenty minutes to complete this sample test, then check your answers with those given on page 230.

PART A

DIRECTIONS: Four possible answers are given for each question. Choose that answer which is *most nearly correct.*

3. In the northern hemisphere, the direction of winds around a high-pressure center and around a low-pressure center are respectively

    1. clockwise : clockwise

    2. clockwise : counterclockwise

    3. counterclockwise : clockwise

    4. counterclockwise : counterclockwise

4. At the lowest known temperature (almost absolute zero), every element and every compound except one is a solid. Which one is it?

   1. helium
   2. hydrogen
   3. nitrogen
   4. oxygen

5. The term *molecular engineering* refers to

   1. control of chemical reaction through electronic computors
   2. designing of nuclear reactors
   3. developing chemical compounds to fit specific needs
   4. developing industrial materials from farm crops

19. A level of 160 decibels, a very loud noise, has been found lethal for some animals. This occurs through

   1. causing malfunction of the liver
   2. impairment of hearing
   3. raising body temperature
   4. reduction in sleep

20. Yttrium's advantage in the nuclear field is "its relatively low thermonuclear cross section." This means that

   1. it has less resistance than many other materials to the passage of neutrons needed to sustain a nuclear reaction
   2. it is highly resistant to the passage of neutrons
   3. it takes very little of this material to contain an active reactor cell
   4. its melting point is high enough to withstand reactor temperatures

21. A *Venn* diagram is the graphical representation of

   1. a cross section of a plant's stem or leaves
   2. the air flowing over an airplane wing
   3. the efficiency of a pump
   4. the relationships between sets

22. Zeolite crystals are *not* useful as

   1. carriers for volatile catalysts
   2. dehydrating devices
   3. semiprecious gems
   4. separators for different types of molecules

PART B

SECTION G

It has been generally accepted that color vision is congenitally determined, that there is little change with age (principally in blue discrimination due to the effects of increasing pigmentation in old age) and that young people should have the best color discrimination.

Lakowski's recent study shows that red-green color discrimination is at its best at about the age of 28, that yellow-blue discrimination is superior around the age of 20; it suggests that children of 10 have poorer red-green discrimination than they will again have until they reach 50. Impairment of yellow-blue discrimination does occur after 25 but more severely than is generally supposed. Violet-bluegreen discrimination shows a surprising change in early childhood and diminishes very sharply after 40 or 45.

QUESTIONS ON SECTION G

50. Which of the curves in the accompanying diagram *best* represents the relationship of age and red-green discrimination?

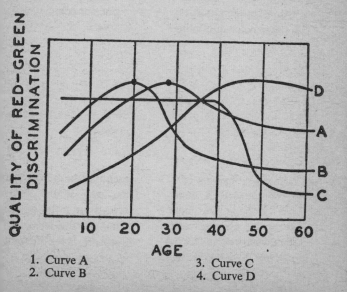

1. Curve A
2. Curve B
3. Curve C
4. Curve D

51. The typical pattern of growth and decline of discrimination with age is
    1. good-good-poor
    2. good-poor-good
    3. poor-good-good
    4. poor-good-poor

ation in early childhood does not mean poor color discrimination as an adult.

4. There is greater age difference than sex difference in ability to discriminate color.

52. On the basis of the paragraphs, which of the following statements is *most* nearly true?
    1. More people have poor yellow-blue discrimination than have poor red-green discrimination.
    2. Older adults have less adequate color discrimination than persons in their thirties.
    3. Poor color discrimin-

53. "Color discrimination is congenitally determined and hence it remains fairly constant throughout the life of an individual." According to the paragraphs this statement is
    1. consistent with experimental results
    2. false
    3. generally accepted but not true
    4. true

PART C

101. Below is a diagram of a vertebrate eye. A number of parts are indicated by arrows, each identified by a letter. For

each part in the list, put the letter of one of the arrows in front of the name of the part indicated by the arrow.

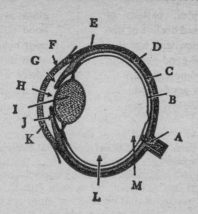

——1. aqueous humor   ——4. lens
——2. cornea   ——5. retina
——3. iris   ——6. sclerotic coat

( ) 2. Alexis Carrel
( ) 3. Heinrich Hertz
( ) 1. Svante Arrhenius
( ) 4. Dimitri Mendeleev

Column II

Column I

1. developed theory of electrolytic dissociation
2. devised the quantum theory of light
3. discovered argon, neon, xenon, krypton
4. discovered methods of tissue culture
5. formulated electromagnetic theory of light
6. initiated the periodic table of the elements
7. measured the charge of the electron
8. produced first wireless waves

103. Select the number of the achievement mentioned in Column II and write it in the parentheses at the left of the name of the scientist in Column I who is associated with it.

For a complete aptitude examination, send 15¢ in coins to Science Clubs of America, 1719 N St., N.W., Washington 6, D. C., and ask for the test.

Science Exam Answers

ANSWERS TO PART A—
two points for each: 3-2, 4-1;
5-3; 19-3; 20-1; 21-4; 22-3.

ANSWERS TO PART B—
two points for each: Section
G: 50-1; 51-4; 52-2; 53-3.

ANSWERS TO PART C
—one point for each: 101.1-
G; 101.2-K; 101.3-J; 101.4-I;
101.5-B; 101.6-E. 103.1-1;
103.2-4; 103.3-8; 103.4-6.

If you have answered all of these questions correctly, you
fared better than any of 203 Science Talent Search contestants
selected at random.

Awarding two (2) points for each correct answer in Parts
A and B, and one (1) point for each in Part C, a high score
on the short version would be 18-20 or more out of a possible
total score of 32. A low score would be 13 or less.

You should not be discouraged if your score is not "glitter-
ing." The test is intended to qualify only the best among
thousands of students, and no one ever has made a perfect
score. In addition, you probably are not as thoroughly in the
test-taking groove as a high school senior who has just finished
college entrance examinations and a number of qualifying
tests for various purposes.

Junior Academies of Science

Among the variety of activities carried on by Junior Academies of Science are: sponsoring and organizing regional
science fairs affiliated with the National Science Fair-International; holding science congresses during which students
present scientific papers and are awarded medals or other
prizes; and organizing field trips, science seminars, lecture
series and career and project counseling sessions.

Many senior Academies conduct state Science Talent
Searches in cooperation with the national Search, awarding
honors, prizes and scholarships to contestants within their
states.

National Merit Scholarships

National Merit Scholarships are four-year college scholarships available to high school seniors. The stipend accompanying each scholarship is based on need and may vary from

$100 to $1500 a year. The average stipend is now about $750 a year. Registration for the Merit Scholarship Program is by high school. The National Merit Scholarship Qualifying Test, the first step in the annual competition, is administered to second-semester juniors and first-semester seniors in the spring of each school year. Each principal is sent registration materials in October. Any eligible student may take the examination at the cost of $1.00. Since the inception of the Merit Program in 1955, some $15.5 million in Merit Scholarships have been awarded to 3132 students. For additional information see your principal or write National Merit Scholarship Corporation, 1580 Sherman Avenue, Evanston, Illinois.

Future Scientists of America

For students in grades 7 through 12 there are regional and national awards based on reports of individual projects in science. This competition is sponsored by the American Society for Metals and conducted by the Future Scientists of America Foundation of the National Science Teachers Association. The closing date for entries is in March. Student entry materials are available from National Science Teachers Association, 1201 16th Street, N.W., Washington 6, D. C.

Junior Engineering Technical Society

JETS chapters are sponsored in high schools by local industry and/or professional groups. The program includes a National Project Exposition with awards and scholarships. Pieces of equipment, such as slide rules and drafting sets, are awarded to junior high school project contest winners. College scholarships are awarded senior high school winners. For information, write to JETS, P.O. 589, East Lansing, Michigan.

National 4-H Congress

The 4-H awards program culminates at the National 4-H Club Congress, where hundreds of members receive recognition and awards, many of which are contributed by industry, foundations and organizations. Experience and training in 4-H activities have started or encouraged the scientific interest of many students who have become national winners in science competitions. For information about your local club, contact your county agricultural agent.

Boy and Girl Scouts of America and Campfire Girls

The experiences and training received in the activities and award programs of these organizations have been responsible for the initial interest of many of their members and have encouraged and broadened the scientific interest of many more. Science Explorer units of Boy Scouts of America have been developed in many areas for older boys.

Local Competitions

A great many civic, fraternal, professional, industrial and other organizations conduct competitions of various kinds for awards ranging from medals to college scholarships. Announcement of such competitions is usually made through the school administration and may be posted on the bulletin board in the guidance counselor's office or in classrooms where science courses are taught.

Publication

Once upon a time it was highly improbable, if not impossible, for a high school student to have his work published. Now, however, there are journals edited for, and often by, students. These publications are doing a very professional job of providing a medium of exchange for young people's ideas, techniques and gratifyingly mature research. In several states the senior Academy of Sciences recognizes the quality of student research by occasionally publishing papers prepared by members of the Junior Academy.

In addition, an increasing number of professional journals in specific scientific disciplines and general publications of wide circulation are inviting students to submit reports of their work.

Growing popular interest in the achievements of potential scientists is reflected also in the many feature articles published in magazines and newspapers describing science fairs and congresses, and the projects presented by young participants.

Such limelight is not only pleasant for those it shines upon, but inspiring and helpful to other beginning scientists. If you are interviewed, photographed or asked to explain your project, remember how important your responses may be in terms of encouragement and understanding for others like you.

If you are invited by a publisher to submit your report for consideration, you will want to prepare your paper as professionally as possible, of course. Teachers and scientists usually are very glad to offer advice and constructive criticism on the organization of your paper and the details of its preparation for submission. (The usual form for a scientific paper is outlined briefly in Chapter 2.)

A Sampling of Good Source Books

THESE lists represent a rather random sampling of the thousands of excellent books available. For every title mentioned, a dozen others come immediately to mind.

With the great upsurge of interest in science, new publications are being produced constantly. These samples are intended chiefly as clues that will lead to others by the same author and by other authors in each of the classifications.

For convenient purchase of any U.S. book in print, send a remittance to cover retail price (postage will be paid) to Book Dept., Science Service, 1719 N St., N.W., Wash. 6, D.C.

I. Junior Books

General Science

Adler, Irving. *Fire in Your Life.* Day, 1955, $3.

Adler, Irving. *The Tools of Science.* Day, 1958, $3.

American Association for the Advancement of Science. *The Traveling Elementary School Science Library.* 1959, 25¢.

Barr, George. *Research Ideas for Young Scientists.* McGraw-Hill, 1958, $3.

Cooper, Elizabeth K. *Science in Your Own Back Yard.* Harcourt, Brace, 1958, $3.

Herbert, Don. *Mr. Wizard's Experiments for Young Scientists.* Doubleday, 1959, $2.95.

Hogben, Lancelot. *The Wonderful World of Energy.* Doubleday, 1957, $2.95.

Lewellen, John B. *Boy Scientist.* Simon and Schuster, 1955, $3.95.

700 Science Experiments for Everyone. Compiled by UNESCO. Doubleday, 1948, $3.

Yates, Raymond F. *Faster and Faster: The Story of Speed.* Harper, 1956, $2.75.

Aeronautics

Branley, Franklyn M. *A Book of Satellites for You.* Crowell, 1959, $3.

Coombs, Charles. *Skyrocketing into the Unknown*. Morrow, 1954, $4.

Fisher, James. *The Wonderful World of the Air*. Doubleday, 1959, $2.95.

Kinney, William. *Medical Science and Space Travel*. Watts, 1959, $3.95.

Ley, Willy. *The Conquest of Space*. Viking, 1949, $4.95.

Anthropology

Boyd, William C. *Races and People*. Abelard-Schuman, 1955, $2.75.

Astronomy

Freeman, Mae, and Ira Freeman. *Fun with Astronomy*. Random House, 1953, $1.50.

Schloat, G. Warren. *Andy's Wonderful Telescope*. Scribner, 1958, $2.75.

Zim, Herbert S, and Robert H. Baker. *Stars*. Simon and Schuster, 1951, $1.95.

Biology

Cousteau, J. Y. *The Silent World*. Harper, 1953, $4.75.

Johnson, Gaylord, and Maurice Bleifield. *Hunting with the Microscope*. Sentinel, 1956, 95¢.

Peattie, Donald Culross. *The Rainbow Book of Nature*. World, 1957, $4.95.

Peterson, Roger Tory, and James Fisher. *Wild America*. Houghton Mifflin, 1955, $5.

Botany

Dudley, Ruth H. *Our American Trees*. Crowell, 1956, $2.75.

Fenton, Carroll Lane, and Dorothy C. Pallas. *Trees and Their World*. Day, 1957, $3.25.

Hutchins, Ross E. *Strange Plants and Their Ways*. Rand McNally, 1958, $2.95.

Selsam, Millicent E. *Play with Seeds*. Morrow, 1957, $2.50.

Sterling, Dorothy. *Story of Mosses, Ferns and Mushrooms*. Doubleday, 1955, $2.75.

Zim, Herbert S. *Plants: A Guide to Plant Hobbies*. Harcourt, Brace, 1947, $3.50.

Chemistry

Freeman, Ira M. *All about the Wonders of Chemistry*. Random House, 1954, $1.95.

Irwin, Keith G. *The Romance of Chemistry from Ancient Alchemy to Nuclear Fissions*. Viking, 1959, $3.75.

Seaborg, Glenn T., and Evans G. Valens. *Elements of the Universe*. Dutton, 1958, $3.95.

Electricity and Electronics

Bendick, Jeanne, and Robert Bendick. *Television Works Like This*. McGraw-Hill, 1959, $2.75.

Freeman, Ira M. *All about Electricity*. Random House, 1957, $1.95.

Lewellen, John. *Understanding Electronics: From Vacuum Tube to Thinking Machine*. Crowell, 1957, $3.

Morgan, Alfred. *Boys' Second Book of Radio and Electronics*. Scribner, 1957, $3.

Engineering

Meyer, Jerome S. *World Book of Great Inventions*. World, 1956, $3.95.

Geology

Pearl, Richard M. *Rocks and Minerals*. Barnes and Noble, 1955, $1.95.

Shuttlesworth, Dorothy. *The Story of Rocks*. Doubleday, 1956, $2.95.

Sterling, Dorothy. *The Story of Caves*. Doubleday, 1956, $3.

Mathematics

Adler, Irving. *Magic House of Numbers*. New American Library, 1958, 35¢.

Hogben, Lancelot. *The Wonderful World of Mathematics*. Doubleday, 1955, $2.95.

Sticker, Henry. *How to Calculate Quickly*. Dover, 1956, $1.

Medicine

Calder, Ritchie. *The Wonderful World of Medicine*. Doubleday, 1958, $3.95.

Cooley, Donald. *Science Book of Wonder Drugs*. Watts, 1954, $3.50

Reinfeld, Fred. *Miracle Drugs and the New Age of Medicine*. Sterling, 1957, $3.95.

Schubert, Jack, and Ralph E. Lapp. *Radiation: What It Is and How It Affects You*. Compass, 1958, $1.25.

Meteorology

Laird, Charles, and Ruth Laird. *Weathercasting*. Prentice-Hall, 1955, $3.95.

Wyler, Rose. *The First Book of Weather*. Watts, 1956, $1.95.

Physics

Atkin, J. Myron, and R. Will Burnett. *Electricity and Magnetism*. Rinehart, 1958, $1.

Boys, Charles V. *Soap Bubbles*. Dover, 1959, $1.

Haber, Heinz. *Our Friend the Atom*. Dell, 1956, 35¢.

Irving, Robert. *Energy and Power*. Knopf, 1958, $2.75.

Irving, Robert. *Sound and Ultrasonics*. Knopf, 1959, $2.75.

Paschel, Herbert P. *The First Book of Color*. Watts, 1959, $1.95.

Ruchlis, Hy. *Orbit*. Harper, 1958, $2.75.

Physiology

Glemser, Bernard. *All about the Human Body*. Random House, 1958, $1.95.

Schneider, Leo. *Lifeline: The Story of Your Circulatory System*. Harcourt, Brace, 1958, $2.95.

Zoology

Berrill, N. J. *The Living Tide*. Premier, 1956, 35¢.

Carson, Rachel. *The Edge of the Sea*. New American Library, 1959, 50¢.

Cruickshank, Allan, and Helen Cruickshank. *1001 Questions Answered about Birds*. Dodd, Mead, 1958, $5.

Lavine, Sigmund A. *Wonders of the Hive*. Dodd, Mead, 1958, $2.95.

Scientific American, Editors of. *Twentieth Century Bestiary*. Simon and Schuster, 1955, $1.45.

Zim, Herbert S., and Hurst H. Shoemaker. *Fishes*. Golden Press, 1957, $1.

II. Senior Books

General Science

American Association for the Advancement of Science, and National Science Foundation.
  The AAAS Science Book List. 1959, $1.
  An Inexpensive Science Library. 1959, 25¢
  A Selected List of Career Guidance Publications for High School Students. 1959, free.
  The Traveling High School Science Library, 5th ed. 1959, 25¢.

Asimov, Isaac. *Only a Trillion: Speculations and Explorations on the Miracles of Science.* Abelard-Schuman, 1957, $3.50.

Calder, Ritchie. *Science in Our Lives.* Signet Key, 1955, 35¢.

Campbell, Norman. *What Is Science?* Dover, 1952, $1.25.

Gamov, George. *One, Two, Three . . . Infinity: Facts and Speculations of Science.* Mentor, 1953, 50¢.

Goldstein, Philip. *How to Do an Experiment.* Harcourt, Brace, 1957, $2.60.

Schrödinger, Erwin C. *Science, Theory and Man.* Dover, 1957, $1.35.

Science Service. *Science Exhibits.* 1959, $2; *Scientific Instruments You Can Make.* 1954, $2.

Standen, Anthony. *Science Is a Sacred Cow.* Everyman, 1950, $1.15.

Thomson, J. Arthur. *Riddles of Science.* Premier, 1958, 50¢.

Weyl, Hermann. *Philosophy of Mathematics and Natural Science.* University Press, Princeton, 1959, $1.95.

Aeronautics

Bizomy, M. T., ed. *The Space Encyclopedia.* Dutton, 1957, $6.95.

Ley, Willy. *Satellites, Rockets and Outer Space.* New American Library, 1958, 35¢.

Agriculture

Archer, Sellers C. *Soil Conservation.* University of Oklahoma, 1956, $3.75.

Cook, J. Gordon. *The Fight for Food.* Dial, 1957, $3.

Astronomy

Clason, Clyde B. *Exploring the Distant Stars*. Putnam, 1958, $5.

Degani, Meir H. *Astronomy Made Simple*. Doubleday, 1955, $1.

Hoyle, Fred. *Frontiers of Astronomy*. New American Library, 1957, 50¢.

Schroeder, Wolfgang. *Practical Astronomy*. Philosophical Library, 1957, $6.

Shapley, Harlow. *Of Stars and Men*. Beacon, 1958, $3.50.

Texereau, Jean. *How to Make a Telescope*. Interscience, 1957, $3.50.

Astrophysics

Eddington, Arthur. *The Expanding Universe*. University of Michigan, 1958, $1.45.

Gamow, George. *The Birth and Death of the Sun*. New American Library, 1952, 50¢.

Bacteriology

Cook, J. Gordon. *Virus in the Cell*. Dial, 1957, $3.

Biology

Beck, William S. *Modern Science and the Nature of Life*. Harcourt, Brace, 1957, $5.75.

Callison, Charles H., ed. *America's Natural Resources*. Ronald, 1957, $3.75.

Hoffman, Joseph G. *The Life and Death of Cells*. Doubleday, 1957, $4.50.

Kleiner, Israel S., and James M. Orten. *Human Biochemistry*, 5th ed. Mosby, 1958, $9.

Simpson, G. G., C. S. Pittendrigh and H. Tiffany. *Life, an Introduction to Biology*. Harcourt, Brace, 1957, $7.50.

Weisz, P. B. *The Science of Biology*. McGraw-Hill, 1959, $7.95.

Biology—Evolution

Fisher, Ronald A. *The Genetical Theory of Natural Selection*. Dover, 1959, $1.85.

Botany

Graves, Arthur Harmount. *Illustrated Guide to Trees and Shrubs*, ed. Harper, 1956, $6.

Harlow, William M. *Trees of the Eastern United States and Canada*. Dover, 1957, $1.35.

Hylander, Clarence J. *World of Plant Life*. Macmillan, 1956, $8.95.

Scientific American, Editors of. *Plant Life*. Simon & Schuster, 1957, $1.45.

Chemistry

Davis, Helen Miles. *The Chemical Elements*. With revisions by Glenn T. Seaborg. Science Service, Washington, D. C., 1959, 55¢.

Hawk, Burton L. *Experimenting with Chemistry*. Science Service, Washington, D.C., 1957, $2.

Hawk, Burton L. *Organic Chemistry for the Home Lab*. Science Service, Washington, D. C., 1956, $2.

Holmes, Harry N. *Out of the Test Tube*. Emerson, 1957, $4.50.

Hutton, Kenneth. *Chemistry*. Penguin, 1957, 85¢.

Chemistry—Technological

Couzens, E. G., and V. E. Yarsley. *Plastics in the Service of Man*. Penguin, 1956, 85¢.

Diamond, Freda. *Story of Glass*. Harcourt, Brace, 1953, $3.75.

Electrical Engineering

American Radio Relay League. *The Radio Amateur's License Manual*. A.R.R.L., West Hartford, Conn., 1959, 50¢.

Tepper, Marvin. *Fundamentals of Radio Telemetry*. Rider, 1959, $2.95.

Engineering

Steinman, David B., and Sara Ruth Watson. *Bridges and Their Builders*, 2nd ed. Dover, 1957, $1.95.

Geography

Carson, Rachel L. *The Sea Around Us*. Mentor, 1954, 50¢.

Lobeck, Armin K. *Things Maps Don't Tell Us*. Macmillan, 1956, $4.95.

Moore, W. G. *A Dictionary of Geography*. Penguin, 1952, 65¢.

Geology

Adams, Frank D. *The Birth and Development of the Geological Sciences*. Dover, 1954, $1.95.

Bates, D. R. *The Earth and Its Atmosphere*. Basic Books, 1957, $6.

Mathematics

Carmichael, Robert D. *The Theory of Numbers and Diophantine Analysis*. Dover, 1959, $1.35.

Courant, Richard, and Herbert Robbins. *What Is Mathematics?* Oxford, 1941, $6.

Heath, Royal V. *Mathemagic*. Dover, 1957, $1.

Lieber, Lillian R. *The Education of T. C. Mits*. Norton, 1944, $3.50.

Newman, James R. *The World of Mathematics*. (4 Vol.) Simon and Schuster, 1956, $20.

Rademacher, Hans, and Otto Toeplitz. *The Enjoyment of Mathematics*. University Press, Princeton, 1957, $4.50.

Titchmarsh, E. C. *Mathematics for the General Reader*. Anchor, 1959, 95¢.

Wiener, Norbert. *Cybernetics*. John Wiley, 1948, $3.50

Medicine

Hemming, James. *Mankind Against the Killers*. Longmans, Green, 1956, $3.50.

Sproul, Edith E. *The Science Book of the Human Body*. Pocket Books, 1959, 35¢.

Tokay, Elbert. *The Human Body and How It Works*. New American Library, 1957, 50¢.

Meteorology

Cook, J. Gordon. *Our Astonishing Atmosphere*. Dial, 1957, $3.

Microscopy

Corrington, Julian D. *Exploring with Your Microscope*. McGraw-Hill, 1957, $4.95.

Nutrition

Nasset, Edmund Sigurd. *Food and You*. Barnes and Noble, 1958, $1.25.

Photography

Larmore, Lewis. *Introduction to Photographic Principles*. Prentice-Hall, 1958, $6.

Physics

Cook, J. Gordon. *We Live by the Sun*. Dial, 1957, $3.

Lansdell, Norman. *The Atom and the Energy Revolution*. Penguin, 1958, 65¢.

Reinfeld, Fred. *Rays: Visible and Invisible*. Sterling, 1958, $3.50.

Physiology

Riedman, Sarah R. *Our Hormones and How They Work*. Abelard-Schuman, 1956, $2.50.

Psychology

Carmichael, Leonard. *Basic Psychology*. Random House, 1957, $3.95.

Sperling, Abraham P. *Psychology Made Simple*. Doubleday, 1957, $1.

Zoology and Evolution

Baerg, J. *The Tarantula*. University of Kansas, 1958, $3.

Blum, Harold F. *Time's Arrow and Evolution*. University Press, Princeton, 1959, $1.75.

Norman, J. R. *A History of Fishes*. Hill and Wang, 1958, $6.

III. Series

Doubleday Science Program, prepared with the cooperation of Science Service. Monthly booklets on various aspects of science, including *Universe*, *Flight*, *Submarines*. Doubleday and Co., Inc., Science Program, Dept. 9-NR-7, Garden City, N. Y. $1 per month, introductory sample 10¢.

Educational Services Incorporated. The Physical Science Study Committee. PSSC Science Study Series. Several books have been published and many more are under way. Orders should be addressed to the Science Study Series, Wesleyan University Press, Inc., Education Center, Columbus 16, Ohio. Students and teachers may purchase the first 5 books in minimum orders of 10 copies at 65¢ each.

Grade Teacher. Booklets for teachers of science in grade school, primary to upper grades. Educational Publishing Corp., Darien, Conn. Science 1 and 2, $1.25 each. *Science Comes to Life*, books 1 and 2 with liquid duplicator, $2.95 each. *Natural Science*, books 1 and 2, $1.35 each. All have suggestions for classroom experiments. Also *Indoor Gardens*, $1.95, 200 illustrations and complete directions for classroom use.

Science Manpower Project Monographs. General and specific science books available and under way. Monographs may be obtained from the Bureau of Publications, Teachers College, Columbia University, New York 27, N. Y.

Science Research Associates. SRA Modern World of Science Series. These booklets, covering many scientific fields, are prepared cooperatively with Science Research Foundation, Inc. Write to Science Research Associates, 259 E. Erie St., Chicago 11, Ill.

Scientific American paperback series: *Astronomy, Plants*, etc. Scientific American Books, Simon and Schuster, 630 Fifth Ave., New York 20, N. Y.

Space Agency publications. NASA, 1512 H St., N.W., Washington 25, D. C.

Periodical Sources

General

Aviation Week, Including Space Technology. McGraw-Hill, 330 W. 42nd St., New York 36, N. Y., $7.

Current Science and Aviation. American Education Publications, 1250 Fairwood Ave., Columbus, Ohio, $1.40 a year.

Review of Scientific Instruments. American Institute of Physics, Inc., 335 E. 45th St., N. Y. 17, N. Y., $11.

Science. American Association for the Advancement of Science, 1515 Massachusetts Ave., N. W., Washington 5, D. C., $8.50.

Science Digest. 200 E. Ontario St., Chicago, Ill., $3.50 per year; 2 years $6.

Science News Letter. Science Service, 1719 N St., N. W., Washington 6, D. C., $5.50.

Science World. Scholastic Magazines, Inc., 33 W. 42nd St., New York, N. Y., $1.50.

Scientific American. 415 Madison Ave., New York 17, N. Y., $5.

Aeronautics

Missiles and Rockets. 1001 Vermont Ave., N. W., Washington 5, D. C., $5.

Space Age. Quinn Publishing Co., Inc., Kingston, N. Y., $2.50.

Agriculture

Agricultural Research Service. U. S. Dept. of Agriculture, Washington 25, D. C., $1.

Anthropology

The American Anthropologist. American Anthropological Assn., Logan Museum, Beloit, Wis., $12.

American Antiquity. Society for American Archaeology, Salt Lake City, Utah, $8.

Astronomy

Astrophysical Journal. University of Chicago Press, 5750 Ellis Ave., Chicago 37, Ill., $15.

Sky and Telescope. Sky Publishing Corp., 49 Bay State Road, Cambridge, Mass., $5.

Biological Sciences

Biological Abstracts. University of Pennsylvania, 3815 Walnut St., Philadelphia 4, Pa., $100.

Journal of Heredity. American Genetic Assn., 1507 M St., N.W. Washington 4, D. C., $7.

Journal of Molecular Biology. Academic Press, Inc., 111 Fifth Ave., New York 3, N. Y., $14.

Plant Physiology. American Society of Plant Physiologists, Box 2665, University Station, Gainesville, Fla., $12.

Proceedings of the Society for Experimental Biology and Medicine. 139th St. and Convent Ave., New York 31, N. Y., $17.

Botany

Biophysical Journal. Bimonthly, Rockefeller Institute Press,

66th St. and York Ave., New York 21, N. Y. First issue scheduled about September, 1960.

Plants and Gardens. Botanic Garden, 1000 Washington Ave., Brooklyn 25, N. Y., $2.

Chemical Technology

Modern Plastics. Breskin Publications, Inc., 575 Madison Ave., New York 22, N. Y., $7 (including Modern Plastics Encyclopedia issue); 2 years $12; 3 years $17.

Textile Research. Textile Research Institute, Box 625, Princeton, N. J., $25.

Chemistry

Chemical and Engineering News. American Chemical Society, 1155 16th St., N. W., Washington 6, D. C., $6.

Chemistry. Science Service, 1719 N St., N. W., Washington 6, D. C., $4, 2 years $7.

Journal of Biological Chemistry. Williams and Wilkins Co., 428 E. Preston St., Baltimore, Md., $36.

Journal of Chemical Education. Division of Chemical Education of American Chemical Society, 500 Fifth Ave., New York 36, N. Y., $4.

Journal of the American Chemical Society. 1155 16th St., N. W., Washington 6, D. C., $30.

Nucleonics. McGraw-Hill, 330 W. 42nd St., New York 36, N. Y., $8.

Engineering

Chemical Engineering. McGraw-Hill, 330 W. 42nd St., New York 36, N. Y., $3.

Electrical Engineering. American Institute of Electrical Engineers, 33 W. 39th St., New York 18, N. Y., $12.

Engineering and Mining Journal. McGraw-Hill, 330 W. 42nd St., New York 36, N. Y., $4.

Mechanical Engineering. American Society of Mechanical Engineers, 29 W. 39th St., New York 18, N. Y., $7.

The Petroleum Engineer. Petroleum Engineer Publishing Co., 800 Davis Bldg., Dallas, Texas, $8.

Proceedings of the I.R.E. Institute of Radio Engineers, 72 W. 45th St., New York 36, N. Y., $18.

QST Amateur Radio. American Radio Relay League, Inc., 38 La Salle Rd., West Hartford, Conn., $4.

Forestry

American Forests. The Magazine of Forests, Soil, Water, Wildlife and Outdoor Recreation. American Forestry Assn., 919 17th St., N. W., Washington 6, D. C., $6.

Journal of Forestry. Society of American Foresters, Mills Building, 17th St. and Pennsylvania Ave., N. W., Washington 6, D. C., $9.

Geography

Geographical Review. American Geographical Society, Broadway and 156th St., New York 32, N. Y., $9.50.

National Geographic Magazine. National Geographic Society, 1146 16th St., N. W., Washington 6, D. C., $8.

Surveying and Mapping. American Congress on Surveying and Mapping, P. O. Box 470, Benjamin Franklin Station, Washington, D. C., $5.

Geology

Bulletin of the Geological Society of America. 419 W. 117th St., New York 27, N. Y., $15.

Geo Times. American Geological Institute, 2101 Constitution Ave., N. W., Washington 25, D. C., $2.

Journal of Geological Education. Dept. of Geology and Geography, Hunter College, 695 Pacific Ave, New York 21, N. Y., $4.

Journal of Paleontology. Society of Economic Paleontologists and Mineralogists, P. O. Box 979, Tulsa 1, Okla., $15.

Mathematics

American Mathematical Monthly. Mathematical Assn. of America, University of Buffalo, Buffalo 14, N. Y., $8.

Journal of Mathematics and Physics. Massachusetts Institute of Technology, Cambridge 39, Mass., $6.

Scripta Mathematica. Scripta Mathematica Society, Amsterdam Ave. and 186th St., New York 33, N. Y., $4.

Mechanics

Popular Mechanics Magazine. 200 E. Ontario St., Chicago 11, Ill., $3.50.

Science and Mechanics. Science and Mechanics Publishing Co., 450 E. Ohio St., Chicago 11, Ill., $2.50.

Medicine

American Journal of Roentgenology, Radium Therapy and Nuclear Medicine. American Roentgen Ray and American Radium Societies, 327 E. Lawrence Ave., Springfield, Ill., $15.

Circulation Research. American Heart Assn., 381 Fourth Ave., New York 16, N. Y., $9.

Experimental Neurology. Academic Press, Inc., 111 Fifth Ave., New York 3, N. Y., $16.

Journal of Nutrition. Wistar Institute of Anatomy and Biology, 36th St. and Spruce, Philadelphia 4, Pa., $22.50.

Journal of the American Dental Association. 222 E. Superior St., Chicago 11, Ill., $7.

Journal of the American Medical Association. 535 N. Dearborn St., Chicago 10, Ill., $15.

Meteorology

Weatherwise. American Meteorological Society, 3 Joy St., Boston 8, Mass., $4.

Natural History

Audubon Magazine. National Audubon Society, 1130 Fifth Ave., New York 28, N. Y., $5; 2 years $9.50; 3 years $12.

Natural History. The Journal of the American Museum of Natural History, Central Park West at 79th St., New York 24, N. Y., $5.

Pharmacology

Journal of Pharmacology and Experimental Therapeutics. Williams and Wilkins Co., 428 E. Preston St., Baltimore 2, Md., $24.

Physics

American Journal of Physics. American Institute of Physics, 335 E. 45th St., New York 17, N. Y., $7.50.

Bulletin of the American Physical Society. Columbia University, New York 27, N. Y., $5.

Bulletin of the Atomic Scientists. University of Chicago Press, 5750 Ellis Ave., Chicago 37, Ill., $5.

Electronics Illustrated. Fawcett Publications, 67 W. 44th St., New York 36, N. Y., $3.

Journal of Applied Physics. American Institute of Physics, 335 E. 45th St., New York 17, N. Y., $12.

Journal of Molecular Spectroscopy. Academic Press, Inc., 111 Fifth Ave., New York 3, N. Y., $30.

Journal of the Optical Society of America. American Institute of Physics, 335 E. 45th St., New York 17, N. Y., $25.

Physical Review. American Institute of Physics, 335 E. 45th St., New York 17, N. Y., $40.

Physics Today. American Institute of Physics, 335 E. 45th St., New York 17, N. Y., $4.

Popular Electronics. Ziff-Davis Publishing Co., 1 Park Ave., New York 16, N. Y., $4.

Psychology

American Psychologist. American Psychological Assn., 1333 16th St., N. W., Washington 12, D. C., $8.

Of Special Interest to Parents and Educators

Allen, Hugh Jr. *Attitudes of Certain High School Seniors toward Science and Scientific Careers.* Teachers College, Columbia University, 1959, $1.25.

Bowles, Frank H. *How to Get into College.* Dutton, 1959, $1.10.

Brandwein, Paul F. *The Gifted Student as Future Scientist.* Harcourt, Brace, 1955, $2.

Brumbaugh, Florence N., and Bernard Roshco. *Your Gifted Child.* Holt, 1959, $3.75.

Cole, Charles C. *Encouraging Scientific Talent.* College Examination Entrance Board, 1956, $3.50.

Conant, James B. *The American High School Today.* McGraw-Hill, 1959, $1.

Cooper, Russell, Jr., ed. *The Two Ends of the Log: Learning and Teaching in Today's College.* University of Minnesota Press, 1958, $4.

Craig, W. Bradford. *How to Finance a College Education.* Holt, 1959, $1.95.

Cutts, N. E., and N. Moseley. *Bright Children.* Putnam, 1953, $3.95.

De Haan R. E. and R. J. Havighurst. *Educating Gifted Children.* University of Chicago Press, 1957, $5.

Fine, Benjamin, and Lillian Fine. *How to Get the Best Education for Your Child*. Putnam, 1959, $3.95.

French, Joseph L., ed. *Educating the Gifted*. Holt, 1959, $5.50.

Henry, Nelson B., ed. *Education for the Gifted*. University of Chicago Press, 1958, $4.

National Aviation Education Council, Secondary Mathematics Curriculum Committee. *The Arithmetic of Flying: A Resource Unit in Air Age Concepts*. Washington, D. C., 50¢.

National Education Association, Conference Report. *The Identification and Education of the Academically Talented Student in the American Secondary School*. National Education Association, 1958, $1.50.

Sheckles, Mary. *Building Children's Science Concepts: Experiences with Rocks, Soil, Air and Water*. Teachers College, Columbia, 1958, $1.50.

Terman, Lewis M., and Melita M. Oden. *The Gifted Child Grows Up*. Stanford University Press, 1947, $7.50.

Terman, Lewis M., and Melita H. Oden. *The Gifted Group at Midlife*. Stanford University, 1959, $4.50.

Waltz, George H. *What Makes a Scientist?* Doubleday, 1959, $2.95.

Weinlander, Albertina A. *Your Child in a Scientific World*. Doubleday, 1959, $2.95.

Witty, Paul, ed. *The Gifted Child*. Heath and Company, 1951, $5.

Equipment and Supplies

Allied Radio Corporation, 100 N. Western Ave., Chicago 80, Ill. General source for electronics equipment and materials.

Carolina Biological Supply Co., Elon College, N. C. Living and preserved materials.

Central Scientific Co., 1702 Irving Park Road, Chicago 13, Ill. General equipment.

Chicago Apparatus Co., 1735-1743 N. Ashland Ave., Chicago, Ill. General equipment.

Difco Laboratories, Inc., 920 Henry St., Detroit 1, Mich. Culture media and reagents.

Eastman Kodak Co., Rochester, N. Y. Photographic supplies and equipment.

Edmund Scientific Co., 99 E. Gloucester Pike, Barrington, N. J. General equipment.

Fisher Scientific Co., 717 Forbes Ave., Pittsburgh 19, Pa. General equipment.

General Biological Supply House, 8200 S. Hoyne Ave., Chicago 20, Ill. Living and preserved materials.

The Heath Co., 307 Territorial Rd. at Edwards Sq., Benton Harbor, Mich. General equipment and materials for electronics.

Hoeltge Bros., Inc., 1921 Gest St., Cincinnati 4, Ohio. Laboratory animal cages and equipment.

Kepco Laboratories, Inc., 131-36 Sanford Ave., Flushing 55, N. Y. School and industrial electrical laboratory equipment.

Multiplex Display Fixture Co., 911-921 N. Tenth St., St. Louis 1, Mo. Display equipment.

New York Scientific Supply Co., 30 W. 30th St., New York 1, N. Y. Preserved and living materials, and chemicals.

Radio Shack, 730 Commonwealth Ave., Boston, Mass. Science and high fidelity materials.

Research Scientific Supplies, Division of Education Equipment Co., Inc., 126 W. 23rd St., New York 11, N. Y. General equipment.

E. H. Sargent and Company, 4647 W. Foster Ave., Chicago 30, Ill. Special laboratory equipment and supplies for biological and chemical sciences.

Science Associates, 194 E. Nassau St., Box 216, Princeton, N. J. Special instruments and teaching aids for meteorology, astronomy and earth sciences.

Science Materials Center, a division of the Library of Science, 59 Fourth Ave., New York 3, N. Y. General equipment, tools and models.

Science Service, 1719 N St., N.W., Wash. 6, D. C. Things of Science, monthly kits of scientific experiments.

Stansi Scientific Co., 1231 N. Honore St., Chicago 22, Ill. General equipment.

Taylor Instrument Co., Olsen and Ames Sts., Rochester, N. Y. Weather instruments.

Tracerlab, Inc., 1601 Trapelo Rd., Waltham, Mass. Radioactivity apparatus.

Triplett Electrical Instrument Co., 500 Harmon Rd., Bluffton, Ohio. Electrical instruments.

Ward's Natural Science Establishment, Inc., 3000 Ridge Rd. E. Rochester, N. Y. Living and preserved materials, rocks and fossils.

W. M. Welch Mfg. Co, 1515 Sedgwick St, Chicago 10, Ill. General equipment.

Wilkens-Anderson Co., 4515 W. Division St., Chicago 51, Ill. Semimicro apparatus and equipment for chemistry.

Booklets and Pamphlets

American Astronomical Society, c/o J. A. Hynek, Sec., Smithsonian Astrophysical Observatory, 60 Garden St., Cambridge 38, Mass. Leaflet: *A Career in Astronomy*. Free.

American Chemical Society, 1155 16th St., N. W., Washington 6, D. C. Bulletin: *The Chemical Profession—An Educational and Vocational Guidance Pamphlet*. 25¢.

American Forestry Assn., 919 17th St., N. W., Washington 6, D. C. Booklet: *Trees Every Boy and Girl Should Know*. 50¢.

American Optical Co., Instrument Div., Box A, Buffalo 15, N. Y. Booklet: *The Effective Use and Proper Care of the Microscope*. Free.

Atomic Research Laboratory, 10717 Venice Blvd., Los Angeles 34, Calif., Attn. Librarian. Booklet: *Laboratory Experiments with Radioisotopes for High School Science Demonstrations*, revised edition. 50¢.

Eastman Kodak Co., Sales Service Division, 343 State St., Rochester 4, N. Y.. Pamphlets (single copies only; request by name and code number indicated): N-4 *Snapshots and Slides Through the Microscope;* C-20 *Astrophotography with Your Camera*. Free.

Edmund Scientific Co., 101 E. Gloucester Pike, Barrington, N. J. Booklets on how to make projectors, photographic enlargers, telescopes, etc. From 10¢ to $1.

Future Scientists of America, National Science Teachers Assn., 1201 16th St., N. W., Washington 6, D. C. *If You Want to Do a Science Project*. Free. *Student Projects*. 50¢

Chas. Pfizer & Co., Inc., Educational Services Dept., 800 Second Ave., New York 17, N. Y. A 32-p. illus. booklet on the story of fermentation chemistry and antibiotics: *Our Smallest Servants*. Free.

Philips Electronics, Inc., Instruments Div., 750 S. Fulton Ave., Mount Vernon, N. Y. Booklets on topics such as X-ray analysis theory and instrumentation, questions and answers on the electronic microscope, the dispersion of carbon black in rubber. Free.

Radio Corp. of America, RCA Electron Tube Div., Harrison, N. J. RC-19 *Receiving Tube Manual*. 75¢. TT-4 *Transmitting Tube Manual*. $1. SCD-108B *Book on Transistors and Semiconductor Diodes*. 30¢.

Registrar, Registry of Medical Technologists, Muncie, Ind. Booklets: *The Profession of Medical Technology; The Human Cell and the Cytotechnologist*. Free.

Rochester Institute of Technology, Public Relations Office, 65 Plymouth Ave., S., Rochester 8, N. Y. Booklets (single copies): *Care in Industrial Chemistry; Careers in Photography*. Free.

Science Research Associates, 57 W. Grand Ave., Chicago 10, Ill. Booklets concerning various topics such as the electronic brain, smashing the sound barrier, jobs for technicians, better living. Prices vary from 60¢ to $1.60. Slight reductions on numbers of copies for majority of titles.

Science Service, 1719 N St., N. W., Washington 6, D. C. *Sponsor Handbook*. (Free to science club sponsors) $1; *Dental Projects for High School Students*. 25¢; *Thousands of Science Projects*. 25¢; *Edison and Other Experiments You Can Do*. 25¢.

UNESCO Publications Center, New York, N. Y. *Radioisotopes in the Service of Man*. $1.

U. S. Government Publications

Coast and Geodetic Survey, U. S. Dept. of Commerce, Washington 25, D. C. Brochures covering general activities and historical background of this scientific and technical bureau of the Federal Government. Free.

Dept. of Agriculture, Office of Information, Washington 25, D. C. (single copies only). F 1567, *Propagation of Trees and Shrubs;* F 2052, *Better Feeding of Livestock;* L 253, *Raising Laboratory Mice and Rats*. Free.

National Science Foundation, Washington 25, D. C. Publications such as *Scientific Information Activities of Federal Agencies*. Free. Brochures: *Secondary School Student Training Programs*, enabling high-ability high school students interested in science to participate in college-level science mathematics and engineering programs during the summer Free.

Tennessee Valley Authority, Knoxville, Tenn. *Fertilizer Science and the American Farmer*. Free.

U. S. Superintendent of Documents, Government Printing Office, Washington 25, D. C. *Space Handbook: Aeronautics and Its Applications*. 60¢.

The Table of Contents will serve as an index if reference is made to the field of science.

254

THE CHEMICAL ELEMENTS are the fundamental stuff of all creation. This is the authoritative story of their discovery and all that is known of their construction, so simply told that anyone may understand it.

The fascinating array of the building blocks of matter is fully covered, from H for hydrogen to those elements discovered in the atomic era, numbered 93 to 102. And the story of each element, its properties, sources, the most important varieties (isotopes), characteristic compounds, and place in periodic tables, appears here in a clear and readily understandable form.

Completely up-to-date, fully indexed, invaluable for reference, this is an essential, and highly readable, handbook for every student, teacher and professional chemist.

The Chemical Elements

Helen Miles Davis

with revisions by Glenn Seaborg

Science Service * Ballantine Books

208 pages, paperbound   50¢

ORDER FROM: Science Service Inc.
1719 N St. N. W., Washington 6, D. C.
or
Dept. 445, Ballantine Books, Inc.
101 Fifth Avenue, N. Y. 3, N. Y.